HUMAN MOVEMENT

an integrated approach

HUMAN MOVEMENT

an integrated approach

JOSEPH R. HIGGINS, Ed.D.

Associate Professor of Education
Physical Education Department
Teachers College
Columbia University
New York, New York

WITH 32 ILLUSTRATIONS

THE C. V. MOSBY COMPANY

Saint Louis   1977

Cover art by GREG WYATT

The C. V. Mosby Company
11830 Westline Industrial Drive, St. Louis, Missouri 63141

Library of Congress Cataloging in Publication Data

Higgins, Joseph R
    Human movement.

    Bibliography: p.
    Includes index.
    1. Human mechanics.   2. Human locomotion.
I. Title.
QP303.H53   612'.76   76-57714
ISBN 0-8016-2181-X

GW/CB/CB 9 8 7 6 5 4 3 2 1

To the memory of my father,
T. Ward Higgins,
and to my mentor,
John E. Nixon

PREFACE

The intent of this book is to present the reader with a new perspective on the study of human movement. I have attempted to deal with the subject matter related to the *whole* process of human movement. Principles and methods are reviewed and discussed as they apply to the analysis and understanding of human movement. The approach is an integrated one with much of the underlying discussion influenced by perspectives from motor learning, experimental psychology, neuropsychology, kinesiology, biomechanics, and human factors engineering.

The current upsurge of interest in human movement studies makes a book of this kind especially important. The level of presentation is directed toward upperclass undergraduate and graduate students in physical education and others interested in analysis and understanding of human movement. The subject matter is integrated through a view different from current texts and course outlines, and hence, in addition to being an exposition of this new view, the text can also be used in current courses such as movement analysis, motor learning, kinesiology, biomechanics, and neuropsychology of motor control.

Human movement as an area of study of physical activity has traditionally dealt with the analysis of functional human anatomy and the mechanics of sports skills. Most of the material available can be viewed as arbitrarily defined chunks of information. Simple analysis of anatomic and mechanical function of specific movements provides us with only a limited perspective. We know a great deal about the mechanics of the anatomy involved in many specific sports skills, but our knowledge appears to be more limited when answers are sought to the question of how the human motorically adapts to the complex world. There has been little if any effort to establish a unifying integrative approach in the study of human movement. It is *not* my intent to rehash traditional materials and approaches; instead my hope is to provide a fresh, multifaceted direction for study. The student, professor, or scholar looking for *tradition* will perhaps be disappointed. It is the complex process of human movement involving interacting and interrelated organizational systems that needs exploration, understanding, and unification. Only then can the teacher or scholar bridge the conceptual gaps between theory, principles, and practice.

In writing this book I have endeavored to close this conceptual gap and provide an integrative approach for studying the complex process of human movement—how the human organism learns to move, the underlying factors leading to the structure of movement, how our movements adapt to simple and complex environmental situations, and how we might proceed in our quest for understanding through a multidimensional technique in the analysis of human movement. Of necessity, seemingly theoretical and empirically based data receive considerable attention when one presents a new and unifying view. I hope the use of examples from practice and sports skills will help the reader attain a reasonable level of understanding for the material and point of view presented.

My approach has been influenced by the Russian neurophysiologist R. N. Bernstein. A structural analysis of human movement is explored as one means of determining the characteristics of movement under differing environmental, morphologic, and biomechanical conditions. The principles of organization of planned, purposeful human movement are developed through understanding the patterns of human movement, the factors influencing skilled motoric adaptation to our environment, and the neuromuscular control processes involved. Acquisition and performance are important conditions of movement production requiring our understanding. Hopefully a multidimensional structural analytic approach may help in achieving this end.

I assume full responsibility for misinterpretations and errors. At the same time I acknowledge a long list of students, colleagues, and teachers who have radically affected my thinking. In particular I wish to acknowledge and thank the members of my Summer 1972 Teachers College, Columbia University, Graduate Seminar in Advanced Biomechanics for their scholarly assistance and critical evaluation of my germinal ideas. My thanks and indebtedness must likewise go to Dr. Ree Spaeth Arnold, Lehman College, City University of New York, who provided scholarly criticism and ideas during the initial draft stages of this book. Professor Susan Arend, Hunter College, City University of New York, is responsible for pushing me to conclude the project, providing a most important substantive and emotional contribution, and has served as my most able editor and critic. Though her influence is felt and gratefully acknowledged throughout the text, Professor Arend's most visible contributions were made in Chapter 9, which deals with tools of analysis. Here she should receive major credit for the model for direct subjective analysis of skill. She has also contributed her artistic talents, as seen in several illustrations throughout the text. The help of my student Francine Rosen is also acknowledged for her assistance during the final manuscript preparation. Finally to my mother and my children, Jillene and Joseph, to Ruth Revett, my former secretary, and to Professors Antoinette M. Gentile and Donald L. Pardew, my humble thanks and gratitude for their constant emotional support and encouragement.

Joseph R. Higgins

CONTENTS

xi

HUMAN MOVEMENT

an integrated approach

ONE

A basic framework for the study of human movement

Our movements provide us with the ability and the means to communicate, to be expressive, to relate to each other, and to learn about and act upon our environment. How we learn about and how we act upon our environment through movement is the broad focus of this book. We will strive to develop an understanding of what our movements can reveal about many of the underlying processes involved in the learning and performance of skilled movements or actions. Our study will lead us toward understanding the factors that are responsible for or regulate the control and coordination of voluntary, goal-directed movement. This chapter is intended to provide a preliminary, basic framework for the more detailed discussion in later chapters.

The range and potential of our movement are suggested by the following quotation:

> Our finest deeds consist only of patterns of muscular-fiber-twitches,
> our greatest printed passages only ink marks on paper, while our most
> ravishing music, as pointed out by William James, is but the rasping
> of hairs from a horse's tail on the intestines of a cat. (Sperry, 1972.)

It is through movement that we reveal our creations, express our feelings, and act upon our environment. Study and understanding of human movement will reveal a great deal about the nature of human behavior: how we move and how we interact with the environment.

The form and grace of the dancer moving across the stage floor, the precision, beauty, and strength revealed in the gymnastic performer's

1

routine on the uneven parallel bars, the quarterback throwing the winning touchdown in the closing minutes of a crucial contest, the high jumper's leap to establish a new world record—these events are not only exciting to watch but demonstrate an almost infinite variety of interacting factors that have contributed to the final product. Identifying these many factors and understanding their potential interactions constitute our major concern.

Highly skilled movement is not the only behavior that we direct our attention to; to the contrary, observation and understanding of movement characterized by a totally different quality can be equally revealing. The movements during the initial stages of learning a new task such as typing and those of a group of young children learning the beginning elements of dance, gymnastics, or basketball reveal information about movement that study of highly skilled movements does not. Likewise, by observing movement in the clinical setting and by analyzing movement in persons with pathologic conditions we can gain insight into the nature of human movement unavailable through observation and analysis of movement in normal skilled or unskilled persons. The uncertain, jerky, uneven, and inconsistent nature of the movements during the initial stages of acquisition of a skill inform us about a very different aspect of how the organism goes about learning the skill—how the information from the environment is gathered, how the movement is planned in relation to the demands of the environment, and how the movement is executed within the context of the performer's morphology, level of fitness, experience, and age.

People interested in the study of human movement must be prepared to think about the range of movement potentialities involving the entire continuum of skill level, types of skill, and settings. At the same time, the many factors that contribute to the production and organization of movement must be studied and understood. In this way we can integrate understanding about the processes and the nature of human movement with questions related to the acquisition of motor skills. The fact that the regularity, precision, and consistency of patterns of movement vary according to level and type of skill is in itself an important point to keep in mind. As we observe movement, whether by visual observation or by means of precise recording and measurement, it is important to identify elements of the movement that are similar and elements that are dissimilar. Understanding these differences and similarities and identifying the consistencies and inconsistencies of skill at the macro or micro level are important aspects of understanding human movement. The present chapter sets forth the basic framework for this notion. The context then is viewed as the movement itself—what the movement looks like, the similarities and differences between elements, the qualitative and quantitative characteristics—and how the movement enhances our understanding of the acquisition and regulation of motor skill; the basic framework is provided through the structural analysis of movement and by the tools, methods, and information of biomechanics and kinesiology and by what is known about the role of the environment, biomechanics, and morphology in control and regulation of movement. Careful analysis of the movement itself in relation to factors thought strongly to influence regulation and control of movement can provide the teacher and the researcher with critical information about motor skill performance and acquisition of skill (Arend and Higgins, 1976). The reader should also develop an appreciation for the contribution of the various disciplines and modes of inquiry that help integrate our understanding of the nature of human movement.

KINESIOLOGY AND BIOMECHANICS

The preparation for teaching of physical education has traditionally included core courses providing a basic scientific orientation or background. Kinesiology is one of the core courses physical education students for the past 20 to 30 years have been expected to master. The term *kinesiology*[1] designates an area of scientific inquiry, the sum of what is known about human movement. It is the study of human movement. Courses and textbooks in kinesiology traditionally emphasize the human anatomy and its functional relationship to the moving organism. More recently the area of biomechanics has been defined as a domain separate from kinesiology, as revealed by the appearance of books dealing with the relation of laws of mechanics and principles of physics to specific sport skills (Hay, 1973; Hopper, 1973; Northrup and associates, 1974). Recently several national and international conferences have dealt with the specialized area and topics in biomechanics (Cooper, 1971; *International seminar in biomechanics II, III, & IV*, 1971, 1973, and 1974).

The emphasis from both kinesiology and biomechanics has been directed largely toward providing a basic understanding of the musculoskeletal system and the laws of mechanics in hopes that the functional aspects of human movement might be better understood and applied to teaching. These efforts are important and have made a significant contribution to our knowledge and understanding of human movement. On the other hand, very little work has been directed toward understanding the underlying processes involved in the regulation of movement or toward viewing these processes through observation of the movement itself. All too often the approach has been to focus on highly skilled performances and then attempt directly to apply what has been learned to teaching and coaching at all levels of skill development. As noble as the attempts have been in identifying optimal patterns of movement, forces, and other biomechanical variables and carefully mapping muscular activity in relation to highly skilled movement performances, they have contributed little to an understanding of how movement is organized and how the elements of movement change in relation to acquisition of skill. Few attempts have been made to integrate principles and concepts from kinesiology and biomechanics to questions related to acquisition of skill and the organization of movement.

Biomechanics is an area of study dealing with the relationship between mechanical and physical principles and the whole biologic system. Implicit in the study of biomechanics is the notion that human movement is the result of a constant interplay between external and internal conditions.

For our purposes the province of biomechanics is best defined by five directions of study and research: (1) the patterns of movement under different regulatory conditions and during acquisition of skill; (2) the organization of movements, motor control processes, and neurophysiology of motor control; (3) the forces and energy produced during movement; (4) the functional aspects of muscular activity in relation to specific movement conditions or skill; and (5) nonverbal communication and psychosomatic phenomena associated with motor acts.

The study of biomechanics begins with the analysis of human motoric behavior and seeks to relate these actions in ways that will lead to more effective teaching of motor skill through understanding the principles and concepts underlying the organization of movement. Of primary concern is developing an understanding of the nature of our goal-directed movement behavior. For the beginning student and teacher the appropriate levels of investigation of human movement are the behavioral and movement levels of observation. The reader should realize, however, that these are not the only levels of analysis nor are they the only ones to be discussed in the following pages.

Biomechanics is traditionally divided into two areas: *statics,* concerned with bodies at rest or forces in equilibrium; and *dynamics,* concerned with the forces producing motion or movement. Our interest is with the area of dynamics. Within the area of dynamics we will limit our study to one of two branches. The branch termed kinematics will provide the primary focus. *Kinematics* is the study of the aspect of human movement concerned with displacement, velocity, and acceleration. It is not concerned with the nature and effects of the forces producing the movement, the focus of the branch of dynamics called *kinetics.* Kinematics is the study of movements alone.

As one means of untangling the complex web of interacting processes involved in the organization of movement, we will look at observable, quantifiable movement parameters studied through kinesiology and biomechanics. Heavy reliance is placed upon the concepts, principles, and tools of analysis employed in biomechanics. Discussion will of necessity rely upon findings, principles, and tools from a variety of fields such as physics, anatomy, neuropsychology, psychology, engineering, anthropology, biology, physical education, and motor learning. The study of biomechanics of human movement and motor skills crosses many disciplines. The next section poses a formulation of a specific domain and mode of inquiry that has as its major focus the study, observation, and analysis of motor skill acquisition and performance.

DOMAIN AND MODE OF INQUIRY: BIOMECHANICS AND HUMAN MOVEMENT

Fig. 1-1 presents a schematic flow diagram representing how the area of study of biomechanics and skilled human movement might be con-

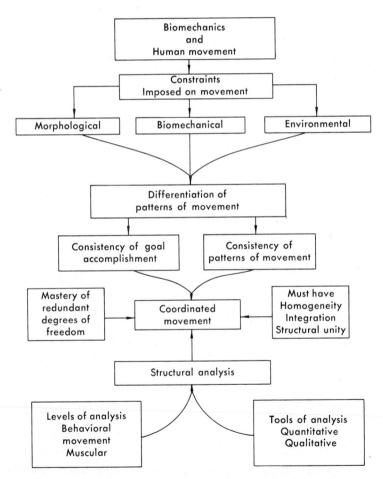

Fig. 1-1. Schematic representation of area of study of skilled human movement.

ceived. Each block of the diagram is dealt with separately either as a chapter or a major section within a related chapter and represents a specific domain concept or mode of inquiry. The central portion of the diagram focuses upon the possible outcome of any single or series of human movements. Observations in the gym, field, pool, stage, or studio reveal a variety of forms of coordinated movement. Coordinated movement can be studied through *structural analysis,* a mode of inquiry involving specific levels and tools for analysis. Our observations may be focused upon the patterns of movement as they relate to consistency of goal accomplishment and consistency of movement. For example, an individual performing the basketball free throw might be viewed with respect to both the outcome or degree of goal accomplishment and the movement that produced the outcome (a basket). As shall be developed in later chapters, the differentiation of distinct patterns of movement reveals a great deal of information about the movement in relation to a variety of conditions called constraints that impose regulatory factors upon the final movement (Gentile et al., 1975; Higgins and Spaeth, 1972).

Biomechanics and human movement as a domain of study and mode of inquiry thus represents a striving to understand coordinated, skilled human movement. All movements are effected and organized in relation to constraints imposed by our morphology, by the performance environment, and by the laws of physics as viewed biomechanically. To arrive at this understanding, a structural analytic approach that focuses upon patterns of movement is employed.

BASIC ASSUMPTIONS

Three important basic assumptions must be set forth to clarify the context and establish a working basis for discussing human movement.

First, the underlying premise is that *there are no fundamental patterns of movement* in the human motoric repertoire. At birth the normal human organism is neurologically "wired" for movement; that is, the organism has the necessary neurologic structures and underlying processes that will enable it to move. As growth and development occur against a background of time and experience, appropriate neurologic control processes emerge allowing the organism to motorically adapt to his environment—plans for action that lead to purposive movement are formulated. In addition, the notion of fundamental patterns of movement implies that there is a uniformity of movement organization. This uniformity would have to permeate a broad spectrum of performance situations. Obviously this cannot be the case, since, for example, all of us have observed wide differences in the manner in which individuals will approach a specific motor task. Also, we have all experienced differences within individuals as they perform a specific task. To say, therefore, that there are fundamental patterns of movement is indeed misleading; it does not account for the multitude of constraints imposed upon the organization of the movement by such factors as the spatial-temporal condition of the environment, the physical laws and biomechanical principles of movement, and the unique morphology of the individual.

A second assumption is that *purposive human movement is regulated by the state of the environment and the state of the organism.* The state of the organism includes the momentary position of the body and limbs as well as the more general morphologic limitations. Closely related to both environmental and morphologic constraints is the biomechanical constraint; that is, the demands imposed upon movement as a result of the effect of physical laws.

The final assumption views human movement within the context of a *self-regulating system.*[2] Human movement provides a vital link in a complex system involving the interaction between the physical world and the organism itself (Higgins, 1972). That is, movements are the result of a complex array of interacting inputs, mediating processes, and outputs. Any movement is thus the result of not only the present state of the organism—such as body and limb position, muscular tension, psychologic states, etc.—but also the condition of the environment and past experience. In addition, our movements are to a certain extent influenced by a long genetic evolutionary history. In a later chapter a multidimensional analytic approach will be discussed that affords the opportunity to simultaneously investigate the movement from four observational levels: behavioral, movement, muscular, and motor. Study of the organization of human movement will thus involve the notion that *movements are the behavioral outcomes of a complex process having to account for the imposition of environmental constraints, biomechanical constraints, and morphologic constraints for each individual performer and each performance trial and task.*

STRUCTURAL ANALYSIS OF HUMAN MOVEMENT

Through years of observing teachers of motor skill and of teaching biomechanics and motor learning to students in physical education and dance, I have been struck by one central problem. Students and teachers of motor skills often lack the keen eye and understanding required for analysis of human movement. The importance of movement analysis for the teacher cannot be overemphasized. Furthermore, much of our research in skill has failed to analyze carefully and meaningfully the very movements and skills we are attempting to teach. The analyses done usually relate to highly skilled performances. Analysis of movement does not provide a way to describe a movement to the student. For example, analysis of high levels of skilled performance has little if any utilitarian value in facilitating motor skill learning during the early stages of skill acquisition (Nixon and Locke, 1973). The importance of the analysis to the teacher and the researcher lies in its process-oriented approach whereby we may expect to achieve a breakthrough between the emerging theories of motor skill learning and the actual practice of teaching.

In an attempt to equip teachers and scholars with better analytic abilities and techniques and to gain a better understanding of how humans develop motor skill, this book proposes a structural analytic approach for the study of human movement. Taking the lead from R. N. Bernstein (1967), this approach is called *the structural analysis of human movement and motor skill.* Relationships are established between the various components making up a movement. Study of the structure of movements provides a way of understanding the functional characteristics from which inferences about the underlying process of organization of movement can be made. The structural analytic approach views the human organism as a self-regulatory system able to receive, encode, process, and transmit information. The study of human movement from this point of view conceives of movement as the integral formations or parts that make up a coordinated, purposeful, goal-oriented movement.

The study of the structure of movements provides an organized way of studying the characteristics of the movements and the underlying process of their organization. The structure is what makes up or constitutes the movement; it is the underlying organizational schema for planned, purposeful, goal-directed movement. By analyzing the components of the movements, we can place the parts of the movement into meaningful, integrated, and useful form. Analysis and observation are directed toward achieving understanding of the spatially and temporally regulated and ordered movement. Of interest, therefore, is the pattern of movement and the observable changes that occur with time, that is, the observation of how a pattern of movement *differentiates* as skill improves and as differing conditions of the environment are imposed upon performance. Patterns of movement and differentiating patterns of movement can be systematically viewed through a trained eye or by means of a number of modern and accurate recording devices that store information concerning acceleration, velocity, and displacement of the body and limbs.

By necessity the structural analysis of movement and motor skill will demand that attention be turned toward analytic and observational tools, identification of underlying principles and processes of coordinated human movement, classification of movement, levels of analysis, and understanding of the different types of constraints regulating the pattern of movement.

STUDY OF HUMAN MOVEMENT

The statement that movements are the only means by which the human organism can interact or operate upon the environment is fundamental to our discussion (Bernstein, 1967:114; Sherrington, 1961). Movements are the only means by which the organism can act upon the environment and are the sole means available for expressing the life activity of the organism. As we study human movement, we quickly realize that it involves actions made in and upon our environment, actions that involve both time and space.

Motion is the progressive change of position in space, time being an implicit concomitant. Movement, therefore, is viewed as a series of muscular actions leading to a progressive change in position in time and space, directed toward accomplishing a goal. The goal, including subgoals, is regulatory and is usually part of the external environment. The goal of a long jumper, for instance, may be to reach 30 feet. This goal is regulatory in terms of the series of muscular actions that must be accomplished in order to satisfy the goal. It is the systematic satisfaction of specific criteria, or subgoals, through a series of muscular actions that leads to satisfaction of the goal. For example, in the long jump, two subgoals may be to place the right foot on the take-off board and to exert the maximum force on the board at a specific point in time.

The very nature of our behavior determines many of our movement capacities. Changes in body and limb position as we interact with our environment are central to our study. Human movement might thus be depicted as acting and interacting in our physical and sociocultural environment through time and space; our movements are developed and maintained through a highly complex, interacting system. This system is continuously molded and conditioned by spatial and temporal characteristics inherent to the organism and the physical world (Higgins, 1972). This includes environmental, biomechanical, and morphologic constraints.

Motor skill in the context of biomechanics

Since the study of biomechanics is viewed as the context for understanding motor skill acquisition and performance, it seems appropriate to briefly discuss what is meant by motor skill. For a more definitive treatment of skill, the reader is referred to the January 1972 *Quest* (see specifically Gentile) and the October 1972 *Research Quarterly* (see specifically articles by Spaeth, Welford, and Whiting).

There are as many definitions and descriptions of skills as there are writers in the area. Obviously there is no unified or unifying statement that can adequately describe skill. Each of us must determine our own working definition. For our purposes, however, let it suffice to say that *motor skill* is movement that allows the organism to respond or act effectively and efficiently within the environment through bodily or limb manipulative movement. The organism must be capable of integrating sensory information and past experience with appropriate movement responses or actions in order to achieve a particular goal. Motor skill is usually the end product of practice and the process of learning. Motor skill is viewed as being goal directed. Level of skill is determined by the degree to which the goal is achieved, and can be described along a continuum represented by low to high skill.

With respect to degree of goal accomplishment, an important distinction needs to be made. Different types of activities that involve motor skill demand different considerations to determine the degree of goal accomplishment. For example, although the swimmer and the diver may be highly skilled performers, our method of determining skill level will be quite different for each. In speed swimming we are interested in the achievement of an optimal time to cover a specific distance; we are looking for effectiveness and consistency of speed. With respect to movement, the question regarding the relationship between consistency in pattern of movement and biomechanical principles needs to be addressed. For the diver, the critical point is the ability to reproduce the dive given the imposed requirements of execution; form is essential. Here we look for consistency of an imposed pattern of movement. The common denominator in these two examples is *consistency*, one relative to speed and the other relative to form or specified movement.

Finally, it should be noted that motor skills are performed within differing types of environments. The nature of the environment also imposes regulatory and control functions upon the movement. The spatial and temporal nature of the environment will to a considerable extent regulate the character, nature, and organization of the movements that will be effective when acquiring or performing a motor skill. Given the same task but different spatially and temporally ordered performance environments, the emerging patterns of movement will also differentiate in a number of ways; that is, given each environmental condition (spatial and temporal changes), there will be a different pattern of movement even though the task itself is the same (Higgins and Spaeth, 1972). Thus we have another reason to refute the suggestion for fundamental patterns of movement.

It should now be clear that it is the *nature of the movement*—its structure—that the area of biomechanics strives to understand. The study of biomechanics and kinesiology has all too often focused either upon the highly skilled performance or upon a single performance trial. From this we have attempted to make application to teaching and the acquisition of skill. A majority of research in motor learning has focused upon a molecular level with the primary concern being directed toward studying the performance outcomes. Relatively little attention has been directed toward the elements that go together to produce the outcome, that is, toward analysis of the movement itself. Furthermore, studies in the mechanical analysis of skill have reached a plateau of questionable utility with respect to their application to teaching and learning. Little if any study has dealt with answering questions about how movements for a particular activity or skill may change over time, or how the elements composing a skill change with practice. Often we see the teacher attempting to specify form or way of doing a skill based upon the analysis of the highly skilled performer. This is the "ideal form myth" referred to by Spaeth (1972). Continued focus upon the ideal form at high skill levels omits or loses important individualistic aspects of the skill. Analyzing high-level performances tells us nothing about the process of learning a skill. The developmental psychologist Harry Kay (1969) has put it very succinctly:

> Overall time measures showing improvement with age and practice are useful but it is the detailed analysis revealing such features as how the skill is being conducted, how the role of the limbs progressively changes, and how anticipatory responses are established which are now required. The earlier photographic records were important signposts but we now require a stricter measure of the time sequence of the constituent parts to evaluate their contribution to the total skill.

NOTES

1. Kinesio- or kine- is from the Greek *kinesis*, meaning motion; -ology means "the study of."
2. A cybernetic or self-regulating system conceives of man as a link in the complex system involving the interaction between the physical world and the self, the physical environment and the living organism.

TWO

The classification and description of human movement

This chapter deals with the various descriptors and systems for classifying human movements. A workable knowledge of some form of classification system is important for the teacher and researcher of motor skills. Identifying the different ways authors and scientists have classified human movement should provide the reader a clearer conception of the abstract ideas and concepts behind the many types of movements observed in the laboratory, playing field, gym, pool, and dance studio. At its best, classification is a contrived system designed to order our ideas and concepts. If nothing else, it should provide us with an increased command over our present knowledge while providing the basis for acquiring more meaningful information and knowledge. Classification of movement should aid in making decisions relative to structuring the learning environment for movement and provide a means by which decisions can be made about appropriate teaching techniques. More importantly, a sound, workable classification system is a fundamental component in the description and analysis of movement. The classification system chosen has a direct bearing upon the system of analysis chosen. As will be seen, there is also a direct connection between the type of movement and the nature of the performance environment. It is this connection that provides the basis of a workable classification system.

Skill is effective goal accomplishment through movement—bodily or limb manipulative. Movements that comprise skills are series of muscular actions directed toward accomplishing the goal. The classification of movement leads toward a working understanding of skill and contributes immeasurably to our systematic analysis and understanding of human movement. Without some systematic form for classification and categorization of movement, analysis would often prove inappropriate, cumbersome, or perhaps meaningless. For example, it would obviously be inappropriate to attempt to analyze movement in terms of its so called internal representation (motor plan), when in effect we are interested in simply a descriptive analysis of a particular sports skill or dance movement. The basis of a composite model of classification ultimately rests with the interaction between the type of movement and the nature of the environment.

Throughout the history of the study of human movement, scientists and teachers have classified movements and skills in many different ways. Physical educators, kinesiologists, anatomists, psychologists, human factor engineers, and neurophysiologists each have their own classification system. Six systems are identified for the classification of movement or skill: anatomic, purpose, origin, character, physiologic, biomechanic. Each system is appropriate for specific kinds of analysis and very often for specific types of training, performance, learning, teaching, or research. At the same time, each system has its unique limitations (when appropriate these limitations are identified along with the strengths). The classification system presented here is one I believe is in keeping with the major objectives of the book and is certainly fundamental to the proposed forms of analysis of human movement.

MOVEMENTS CLASSIFIED ACCORDING TO JOINT ACTIONS

Anatomists and kinesiologists choose to classify movements in terms of the type of action possible at a particular articulation (joint). The movement is classified according to the cardinal plane in which the movement occurs. The cardinal planes of movement are used as reference points for describing the action or motion of the body or any limb in relation to its associated joint. The planes of motion relate to both the body and each individual joint and are viewed relative to the basic anatomic position. Fig. 2-1 represents an erect body in the anatomic position—body erect, arms at the sides of the body with the palms of the hands facing forward, the feet and toes likewise pointing forward. Each plane of motion for the body is shown: sagittal, frontal, and transverse. These same planes hold for the individual joint, as seen in Fig. 2-2. With reference to the basic anatomic position shown in Fig. 2-1, the following definitions should serve to clarify the direction of movement for both the body as a whole and for each joint: *sagittal*—movement through the anteroposterior plane or section (front to back) that divides the long axis of the body or limbs into right and left; *frontal*—movement through the right-left plane or section that divides the body or limbs front and back;

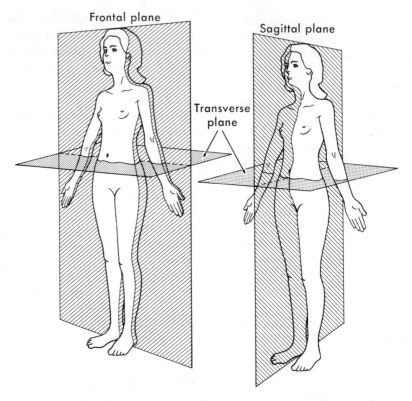

Fig. 2-1. Reference planes of motion for anatomic position.

and *transverse*—movement through a plane or section that crosses the longitudinal axis of the body or limbs (separates the top from the bottom, the upper from the lower). It should be noted that describing and classifying movement using this system involves joint-by-joint determination of the movement. Obviously the real movement or the movement as a whole occurs through several planes; planar movement, in other words, is a descriptor for individual joint or segment action. Each of these planes of motion applies both to the body in its basic anatomic position and to each joint and related segment as seen in Fig. 2-2.

The plane of movement or motion is described in relation to the basic anatomic position, regardless of the position of the joint in relation to the body at any particular point in the total movement. For example, the movement of the knee in Fig. 2-2 is described and classified according to movement at the knee as though the knee were in the anatomic position. The position of the joint and associated limb segments in space and in relation to the body is determined by the planar movement or position of

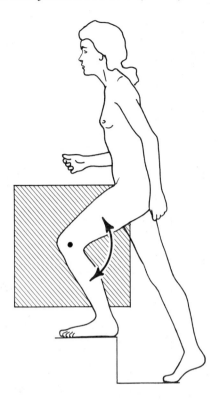

Fig. 2-2. Stepping, with knee action in sagittal plane of motion.

the successive joints making up the movement—usually described as successively progressing from the body midline to the periphery. Describing the movement or position for the shoulder and the trunk (Fig. 2-2) would indicate spatial positioning of the knee with actual movement of the knee being described and classified according to its possible movement with the anatomic position as the referent.

The articular construction—a form of morphologic constraint (Chapter 8)—determines the number of planes through which the limb segments involved can move and the resultant action is the determining factor in the resulting classification system. Each joint can move through one, two, or three planes of movement, depending upon its morphologic construction. For example, the elbow can move through only one plane of motion (sagittal), the wrist and ankle can move through two planes of motion, and the shoulder and hip can move through three planes of motion.[1] Students should familiarize themselves with the possible motions and planes of movement for each joint.

Table 1. Movements classified according to joint action

Plane of movement	Joint actions and definitions	Examples	Primary joints where action observed
Sagittal	Flexion: the angle between two adjacent segments decreases	Elbow when lower arm is brought toward upper arm, as in preparing to throw or in lifting	Wrist, elbow, shoulder, hip, knee, spine, neck
	Extension: the angle between two adjacent segments increases	Knee when lower leg is moving forward in relation to thigh, as when kicking a ball	
	Dorsiflexion: sole of foot and toes pulled up toward leg	Ankle when heel strikes ground in walking	Ankle
	Plantar flexion: sole of foot and toes extended or pointed away from leg	Ankle when toes and feet are pointed, as in diving and gymnastics	
Frontal	Abduction (abd.): segment moves away from midline of body	Shoulder when lifting arm upward and to side away from the body	Shoulder, hip
	Adduction (add.): segment moves toward midline of body	Shoulder when returning arm to side of body	
	Ulnar deviation: hand at wrist moves toward little finger or ulna	Writing with hand alone	Wrist
	Radial deviation: hand at wrist moves toward thumb or radius	Returning the carriage in typing; releasing the register finger when playing the saxophone	

Plane	Movement	Example	Joints
Combined sagittal-frontal	Circumduction: extended segment describes cone shape in space	Wrist when jumping rope; shoulder when employing windmill type underhand pitch in softball	Shoulder,, hip, wrist, spine
Transverse	Rotation: segment moves about its own central axis	Wrist and arm twist when putting spin on a thrown or hit ball; opening a doorknob	Spine, shoulder, radioulnar
	Supination: palm of hand is in anatomic position with reference to arm	Placing hands on floor in preparation for doing push-up	Wrist (hand)
	Pronation: palm of hand is turned or rotated away from anatomic position	Hand position when curling weights or grasping horizontal bar or rings	
	Horizontal (abd.): from position of flexion or extension segment moves away from midline	Shoulder when beginning to pull in breaststroke; backswing in tennis forehand	
	Horizontal (add.): from position of flexion or extension segment moves away from midline	Shoulder when beginning forehand drive in tennis	

Movements of the body and limbs are thus classified according to the actions possible at a specific articulation as that movement occurs in relation to one of three planes of motion. The particular type of movement is classified with reference to the plane of motion for that joint or limb segment. The terms used to describe these actions are listed in Table 1. Once the plane of motion is determined, the joint action can be classified. Examples of each action are given in Table 1 along with the primary joints where the action can be observed. In order to become familiar with this common system of classification and description of movement the reader should spend time practicing using the terms to classify and describe both simple and complex movements used in everyday living and in a variety of sport-type skills.

Each of the terms in Table 1 is briefly stated and defined. Students should consult other resources for a more detailed and definitive treatment of terms (Logan and McKinney, 1970; Rasch and Burke, 1974; Wells and Luttgens, 1976). No attention, for example, is given to the types of hand grips of grasping; these finer points should be obtained from other sources. This system has been most useful in medicine and allied medical fields such as physical and occupational therapy, corrective and adaptive physical education, and care and prevention of athletic injuries. Of primary concern in this system is the description and analysis of isolated joint movements or combinations of relatively few adjacent joints. Anatomists describe the actions of muscles in terms of the classification system here presented, and familiarity with it can therefore facilitate the isolation of specific muscles or muscle groups of interest in movement study. Though kinesiologists in physical education have used this system extensively, it is basically cumbersome and loses its meaningfulness when we are concerned with more complex skills. To be analyzed a movement or skill has to be broken down into such minute components and phases that the slight variations within the skill itself are lost. There are relatively few skills or tasks that involve "pure" flexion or extension, for example; thus this system loses its usefulness when the analysis of complex whole movements is desirable. Finally, the usefulness of the system is limited to descriptive and anatomic analysis of the movement.

Many kinesiologists and physical educators have used this system to aid in the descriptive analysis of highly skilled performance. Here again, what is described for high skill levels may not be appropriate for low skill levels. Furthermore, describing a skill as being composed of a series of flexions, extensions, abductions, and adductions can be of little value functionally in trying to describe how a skill is learned; the primary usefulness of this system relates to describing isolated pathologic conditions and prescriptive exercise for rehabilitation or retraining.

MOVEMENTS CLASSIFIED ACCORDING TO PURPOSE

Some writers classify movements according to the purposes they serve in performing a variety of motor activities (Cooper and Glassow, 1976; Wells, 1971). The basic concern is large muscle activity and sports skills. The skills are classified according to how the body or limbs are used in a particular activity or task. For this system of classification five types of movements are identified: (1) movements for support of the body, (2) movements for suspension of the body, (3) movements for the transport of the body, (4) movements that provide impetus to an external object, and (5) movements that receive an external force. Within each of these classes of movements are subclasses relating to the spatial environment in which the movement is being performed (on a solid surface, in the air, or in the water). Temporal components and combined spatial-temporal components vis-a-vis the movement itself or the environment are not considered. This system fails fully to account for the temporal and spatial constraints that the environment imposes upon the movement. Implied in a classification system of this type is the notion that there are fundamental patterns of movement that can be identified. Because of imposed morphologic and environmental constraints it is unlikely that this system will fully answer our movement analysis and learning questions.

MOVEMENTS CLASSIFIED ACCORDING TO ORIGIN

Several investigators have seen fit to classify movements according to their origin. The basis of this system lies with the dependency of the movement upon the internal and external stimuli that precede or provoke the movement (Bernstein, 1967; Konorski, 1967). This schema is behavioristic in its approach and focuses upon stimuli in relation to the movement produced.

Movements classified according to origin fall into roughly four categories distributed along a continuum of movements. This continuum moves from total dependence upon the external stimulus to more independent movements relying upon greater and greater experience and information processing:

1. *Movements produced as effects of unconditioned reflexes.* These movements are explained in terms of the provoking stimuli. Included here are movements resulting from noxious stimuli or simple reflexes, such as the knee jerk reflex.
2. *Movements produced as a result of an external force administered to the body.* Included here are passive movements.
3. *Movements produced as a sequence of activity having been triggered by a stimulus.* The stimulus is the activator, and the sequence of movements has increasing independence of the stimuli itself. Included here are movements resulting from some form

of conditioning to an internal or external event, such as the immediate reaction when driving, to hit the brakes when a horn honks.

4. *Movements produced without external stimuli playing a decisive role (voluntary movements).* Patterns of movements and the initiation of the movement are determined by the interaction of past experience (learning or programming of movement sequences) and internal and external environmental information.

Classification of movements according to their origin leaves us with a system of analysis related to the effect of the stimuli upon the resultant movement. The system has proved especially useful in identifying and understanding purely reflexive movements.

MOVEMENTS CLASSIFIED ACCORDING TO CHARACTER

Three basic categories comprise the system of classification based on the character of the movements:

1. *Locomotor movements*[3]—the act of changing body position in time and space. Later we shall refer to locomotion as body transport, as in running, skipping, and walking.
2. *Limb manipulation*—"isolated movements of the limbs" (Konorski, 1967). This is the change in position of a limb with respect to the body or other limb segments.
3. *Postural movements*—the body position as in sitting or stooping or jumping. These movements may also involve a more general body stability function.

Movements classified according to character are viewed as nonreflexive, purposeful, and voluntary. As we shall see later, this system will form a critical component for one dimension of the composite classification system. The important aspect of this system is its attention to three basic types of movement. These movements can be combined in several ways in order to provide a wider spectrum of possibilities. For example, a locomotor act can be combined with a limb manipulation movement. In addition, this system is of importance because of its usefulness in the study of motor control and organization of movement (Higgins, 1972; Stark, 1968).

MOVEMENTS CLASSIFIED ACCORDING TO PHYSIOLOGY

Exercise and muscle physiologists have classified movements according to the type of muscular contraction or work involved. Though the physiology of muscle is beyond the scope of this book, it is worth pointing out that movements can also be classified according to the physiology involved.

Three categories are included in this system:

1. *Isotonic contraction or movement.* The muscle shortens during contraction, bringing about a movement of one or more limb segments. The prime function of this type of movement is to accelerate the limb segments.
2. *Isometric contraction or movement.* The muscle contracts but does not bring about a change in position of the limb segments involved. This type of movement is functionally one of fixation. In this category, detectable movement occurs only at the level of the muscle, and no resultant change will occur at the behavioral level. (In order for a fixation movement to occur, contraction of opposing muscle groups must be involved, hence the potential movement effects of any one group are cancelled by another.)
3. *Philometric contraction or movement* (after Hubbard, 1960). The muscle contracts while it is lengthening, sometimes called eccentric contraction. The function of this type of movement is deceleration of the limb segments. Examples of this type of movement occur when the arm is slowed and stopped during the follow-through phase of throwing and when the body is slowly lowered from a horizontal bar. These categories are of most use in planning training programs for the development of muscular strength and endurance. From a biomechanical point of view, this classification system can be useful in certain types of electromyographic study.[4]

MOVEMENTS CLASSIFIED ACCORDING TO BIOMECHANICS

Finally, we can classify movements according to the principles of biomechanics. The primary factors involved in this system are (1) the internal and external forces acting upon the body and limbs to produce the movement, (2) the nature of the space involved during the movement, and (3) the time, or temporal components, of the movement. This schema is most useful in kinetics, the study of forces that produce movement. This system may also serve as a beginning point for identification and use of biomechanical constructs to be discussed in Chapter Three and Chapter Seven.

Movements are categorized in three ways:

1. *Dynamics of the movement*—movements affected by either internal or external forces. Included here are movements affected by the forces of gravity, position of center of gravity, and generated muscular force. These are movements that might be classified according to their kinetic properties. For example, a muscular force might be greater than the external force against which it is applied. The resultant movement will therefore occur in the direction of the applied muscle force.

2. *Spatial characteristics of the movement*—the path described by a limb segment or body in space as described numerically or geometrically. Three basic types of movements can be identified within this category: (1) rectilinear movement—movements in a straight line (in human movement there are no pure rectilinear movements), (2) rotational or angular movements—movements that are angular or curved, as at the joint between two limb segments, and (3) translatory or combined movements—movements that include both rectilinear and rotational components. Walking or performing a somersault in diving are examples of the latter class of movement; the center of gravity of the body will describe a curvilinear path, while the pattern of movement of the limbs may be describing another pattern.

3. *Temporal characteristics of the movement*—the identification of the acceleration and velocity characteristics of a movement and the durational aspects of specific phases of the patterns of movement, for example, identification of movements having uniform velocity as different from movements lacking uniform velocity and acceleration.

This system is most useful when we are concerned with the physical and mechanical aspects of a single sports performance or when the movement is reduced to abstract numerical values for quantification.

COMPOSITE MODEL FOR CLASSIFICATION OF MOVEMENTS AND SKILL

Two points should now be clear: (1) the author's bias in relation to a workable classification system that will account for both the type of movement and the nature of the environment and (2) the realization that each of the systems described has evolved within a specific investigatory approach. Each system has had its value in studying human movement and has developed in relation to a specific approach. No single classification system can be expected to have universal appeal.

Of major importance, however, is a system that can simultaneously provide for the structure of the movement and can incorporate a way of viewing the important dimensions of environment. In this context, a system that will at the same time provide for the type of movement and the nature of the environment is useful.

A three-dimensional system that relates *type of movement* and the *nature of the environment* can easily be constructed. Conceivably each dimension can be used independently as suggested in the preceding sections, but interaction of two or three dimensions offers a useful schema for classification. Credit for the major conceptual synthesis of this system is due my colleague, Professor A. M. Gentile.[5] In a unique way, she has formulated a classification system that includes morphologic and environmental factors as important considerations for a taxonomy of perceptual-motor tasks or skills. The system allows placement of any type of direct adaptive movement or motor skill into a class defined by the type of movement, nature of the environment, and independent temporal control.

To begin with, let us look at some underlying concepts. We believe that movement is organized on the basis of imposed regulation by the environment. This control is within the limits of general and specific morphologic constraints. As stated earlier, our interest is primarily in goal-directed adaptive movements. Goal-directed movement can be of two general types: *indirect* and *direct.* Adaptive movements are those movements by means of which a goal is accomplished. Movements that are communicative, such as speech, gestures, and facial and body expression, are of the indirect adaptive type. Direct adaptive movements are movements by which the organism alters the environment in relation to itself (Gentile, 1972). Though the tools of biomechanical analysis are of equal usefulness in the study of both types of adaptive movement, our concern will be primarily with direct adaptive movements. (A brief discussion of indirect movements will be presented in a later chapter when attention is directed toward biomechanical study of *kinesics*, or nonverbal communication.)

The organism uses directed adaptive movements to alter its position in the environment or to act upon the environment in such a way as to alter the environment itself. These changes within or upon the environment are brought about by altering the position of the body in time and space or by manipulating the limbs in relation to the position of the body. When movements are classified according to their character, three types of movements are identified: locomotor movements, postural movements, and limb manipulative movements. Let us now refer to locomotor movements as *body transport*, postural movements as *body stability*, and limb manipulative movements as *limb manipulation*. It is the character of the movement that in part reflects morphologic consideration.

One dimension of the classification system occurs by combining these three generic types of movement into four subclasses of movement:
1. Body stability without limb manipulation.
2. Body stability with limb manipulation.
3. Body transport without limb manipulation.
4. Body transport with limb manipulation.

All patterns of movement for direct adaptive movements skilled or otherwise will fall within these movement-type subclasses. A simple movement skill classification system can be formulated that allows us to catego-

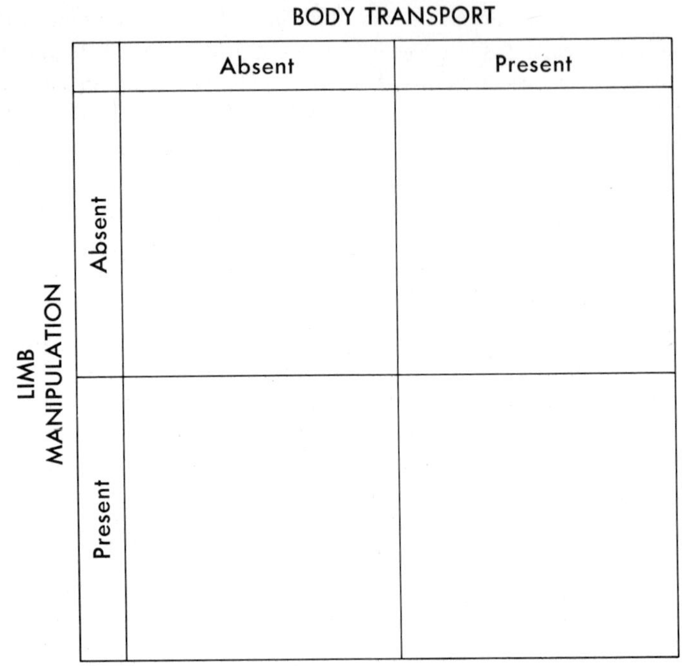

BODY TRANSPORT

	Absent	Present
Absent		
Present		

(left axis label: LIMB MANIPULATION)

Fig. 2-3. Character of the movement. Classification based upon locomotion and limb manipulation interaction.

rize skills according to nature of body transport and limb manipulation (Fig. 2-3).

The second classification dimension (which can be combined with that in Fig. 2-3) relates to the type of regulatory control imposed by the environment. The environment is viewed as a continuum representing varying degrees of spatial and temporal regulation and predictability. That is, at one end of the continuum the environment is relatively stationary or certain and the performer can easily predict what the conditions will be from moment to moment. Skills classified on this end of the continuum have been referred to as closed skills. For example, when hitting a golf ball the performer can with a high degree of confidence, make the prediction, that the ball will not change position prior to his hitting it—the environment is stable. Predictions about how the movement must conform to the environment can be made with a high degree of certainty.

At the other end of the continuum the environment is not stationary; with reference to the performer's ability to predict the condition of the environment, the environment is uncertain. The regulatory conditions

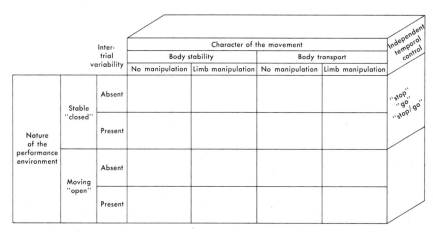

Fig. 2-4. Classification of skill by movement and environment interaction. (Adapted from Gentile et al., 1975.)

are ever changing, uncertain. Skills at this end of the continuum are referred to as open skills. For example, a tennis player must perform within a changing, uncertain environment; tennis is thus an open skill. In this case the opposing player as well as the ball are moving. The movements required in order to hit the ball, are organized and regulated on the basis of predictions about the speed, trajectory, and location of the ball at a particular moment in time. Dividing the environmental continuum is purely arbitrary and does not make for absolute points of departure and interpretation, as can be seen when the model is presented shortly.

The third dimension, independent temporal control, is composed of regulatory environmental conditions that indicate go, stop, or stop-go signals. The starters gun, the time limit in football and basketball games, traffic lights, and so on are examples of independent temporal control. They regulate independently the onset, duration, or termination of certain skills; that is, they regulate independently because movements do not have to conform spatially to these signals. The movement itself, how it looks, is organized independently of the signal.

Fig. 2-4 illustrates in a three-dimensional array the combination of the type of movement, nature of the environment, and independent temporal control. Any movement or skill can fit into this classification scheme. At first the student may encounter some difficulty with the environmental dimension because the continuum has, for the sake of convenience, been divided into two types of control: (1) spatial control, where the environment is stationary; and (2) temporal-spatial control, where the environment is changing. Therefore, when studying Fig. 2-4, keep in mind that the examples are classified according to an abritrarily divided continuum of environmental control, that is, closed and open type skills (Knapp, 1963; Poulton, 1957; Spaeth, 1972). The classification system depicted in Fig. 2-4 has undergone several modifications (Gentile et al., 1975). Careful consideration of the figure reveals that for both closed and open skills there is an additional dimension indicating two variables. These two variables reflect the absence or presence of environmental change from one trial to the next (intertrial variability). For example, how does one account for a skill in which the environment is stationary during the execution of the movement on one trial but changes spatial location before the next trial—as in the high jump where the bar remains stationary during the trial but is raised on subsequent trials (depending upon the success of the individual jumper)? Given this modification Table 2 is based entirely upon the nature of environmental control. This table uses the task of hitting a baseball to illustrate the four possible classification categories derived from the interaction of environmental control and intertrial variability. Each category is mutually exclusive, and category 4 has three subcategories based on the possible permutations of environmental conditions. Table 2 is included to aid the reader in understanding the intertrial variability dimension in Fig. 2-4.

When environmental regulation is the primary dimension for classification, both Fig. 2-4 and Table 2 are illustrative of the notion of two broad categories of skill: closed and open. We shall deal with this important notion in more detail in Chapter Six. To summarize, the broad category of closed skills is defined as including two types of task conditions:

1. "closed" tasks as defined initially involving stationary and stable environments and
2. "limited interaction" tasks involving stationary or moving environments that vary from trial to trial primarily in terms of one dimension, that is, spatially or temporally but not both concurrently. (Gentile et al., 1975.)

Open skills involve regulatory "environmental conditions that involve moving and variable environments" (Gentile et al., 1975).

This classification scheme provides the basis for much of the conceptual and analytic material covered in the remaining chapters of this book. The underlying principles suggested by this classification system have a direct relationship to the study of movements or skill—the nature and character of the movement, the nature of the environment, and independent temporal control as important factors in the regulation of movement. It should be understood that even though there are these broad categories for classification, it is important to think in terms of the sub-

Table 2. Classification of skill based upon environment and intertrial variability*

Nature of environmental control	Intertrial variability	
	Absent	*Present*
Stationary	*Category 1* Batting off stationary tee that remains in one fixed position (Environment is stationary with fixed "target" location from trial to trial)	*Category 3* Batting off stationary tee with height of tee varied from one attempt to the next (Environment is stationary with spatial location varied from trial to trial)
Moving	*Category 2* Batting ball pitched by machine at single fixed rate and flight pattern (Target object in environment is is moving with speed and spatial location fixed from trial to trial)	*Category 4* Batting ball pitched by machine: (Target moving) 1. At one fixed speed but with different flight pattern trial to trial (Spatial location fixed with speed varied from trial to trial) 2. At different speeds with same flight pattern trial to trial (Speed of target fixed with spatial location varied from trial to trial) 3. With variation in both speed and flight pattern from trial to trial (Target speed and location covaried from trial to trial)

*Adapted from Gentile et al., 1975.

categories and finer classifications within each broad type. For this reason it is suggested the reader work through both Fig. 2-4 and Table 2 for as many skills and movements as possible. Practice now will provide dividends later, as our attention turns toward analysis.

NOTES

1. The number of planes of motion possible at each joint will be referred to in subsequent chapters as *degrees of freedom of motion.*

2. An easy way to remember the positional relations of the hand is that supination sounds like soup in hand; that is, in relation to the forearm the hand is in a position to carry soup.

3. For our purposes, locomotion is defined as purposeful maladjustment of the body resulting in a change in base of support.

4. Electromyography is a tool for analysis of the electrical activity of muscles. It is an important tool in biomechanics and will be discussed more fully in Chapter Nine.

5. Professor Gentile is an Associate Professor of Psychology and Education, Teachers College, Columbia University. Her system is formulated on the basis of work by E. C. Poulton, P. Fitts, K. U. Smith, K. Lorenz, and J. Bruner. The theoretical basis for this system can be found in Gentile (1972), and a more detailed treatment of the classification system and its modification can be found in Gentile et al. (1975).

THREE

Coordination of human movement

The study of human movement and skilled motor behavior involves understanding the nature of spatially and temporally coordinated movement—the structure of movement. Understanding coordinated movement aids in the identification of the underlying processes involved in the production of spatially and temporally coordinated skilled movements and in the structural analysis of motor acts.

We shall begin by discussing the nature and the meaning of coordination, what it represents within the context of biomechanics and skill, and how structural analysis of movement is a viable approach for the study of human movement. We are continuing our search for understanding and meaning of human movement through analysis of the self-regulating system responsible for coordinated, adaptive human movement. Within this framework, patterns of movement and the concept of differentiation of patterns of movement will be introduced. Finally, our concern is with the biomechanical constructs that have an important relationship to coordinate movement and its structural analysis.

WHAT IS COORDINATION OF MOVEMENT?

Coordination is the mastery of "redundant degrees of freedom of movement within a kinematic chain of movement" (Bernstein, 1967:127). Coordinated movements are viewed as our "means of ensuring responsiveness and flexibility" of movement activity within the context of the self-regulating system as our actions are directed toward a goal in the environment. Coordination is *not* an independent act directed at the external world but instead is what we can view through movement observation and analysis as a peripheral manifestation of a series of movements that are the result of a complex organization and interactive process. The process involves the integration of experience, central nervous system activity (memory, planning, and information processing), biomechanical factors, and conditions of the morphology and the environment. If these factors are considered dependent variables, coordination can be said to involve decreasing these dependent variables. In other words, as the organism develops skill in a particular sport, manipulative activity, or task of daily living, each factor or dependent variable comes under increased control. An essential feature in understanding coordination is the recognition that the movements we observe are the result of a complex organization and that this organization has meaning because of the control exercised over this vast array of dependent variables. This notion of coordination and overcoming the redundant degrees of freedom or decreasing dependent variables controlling movement grows out of the realization of the inadequacy of the reflex arc as the basis for the processes responsible for control of our movements.

One of the major dependent variables under the organism's control is the degrees of freedom of movement. The degree of freedom of movement is determined by the number of planes of movement a limb segment can move through a particular articular surface. Depending upon the articulation involved and the number of perpendicular planes in which the movement is carried out, degrees of freedom may be one, two, or three. (See Fig. 2-1 for review of planes of motion.) For example, there is one degree of freedom of movement at the elbow articulation (ulnohumeral articulation). The arm at the elbow, therefore, moves through only one plane of motion. For the wrist (radiocarpal articulation) and ankle (talofibular-tibular articulation) there are two degrees of motion possible. The motion possible is through two planes: for the wrist, the sagittal plane (flexion and extension) and the frontal plane (lateral deviation); for the ankle, the sagittal plane (dorsiflexion and plantar flexion) and the frontal plane (inversion and eversion). There are three degrees of freedom of movement available at the hip (acetabular-femoral articulation) and at the shoulder (glenohumeral articulation). This means that the femur and the humerus can move through the three perpendicular planes of motion. The femur and the humerus can be moved forward (extension) and backward (flexion) through the sagittal plane; they can also move from side to side in the frontal plane (abduction and adduction); and they can rotate or twist about their own axis (rotation) in the transverse plane producing an additional degree of freedom of movement. Adding each of these degrees of freedom of motion we determine that the shoulder and the hip each have three degrees of freedom of movement. In order for coordinated movement to occur, these degrees of freedom of movement have to be controlled or regulated. This control is achieved through the modulation of muscular forces at each articulation.

The body is comprised of a "collection of mechanical linkages . . . connected by joints having a variety of freedom of movement" (Roebuck, 1968). (The terms "link" and "segment" are used interchangably to indicate the rigid moving parts of the body, such as limbs, fingers, and trunk. Link is used in the human engineering fields to indicate a rigid part connected to another rigid part with the movement between them possible in a variety of directions.) For any movement, coordination is achieved not only by proper modulating of the muscular forces but also by proper sequencing of the participating links. For example, young children learning to throw objects will exhibit improper linkage or segmental sequencing, thus producing a movement that not only looks awkward but also one that by all accounts would be ineffectual.

Each movement can be described as having a *kinematic chain* of movement that is the sum of all the participating segments. One important aspect of understanding and analyzing movement is evaluating the temporal and spatial aspects within the kinematic chain under study. We need to determine either qualitatively or quantitatively the relationships between each participating link or segment. The structural analysis of coordinated acts calls for this determination in terms of temporal and spatial parameters for displacement, acceleration, velocity, or force. As we shall see later, the analysis can also be extended by employing electromyographic techniques of evaluation to determine the consistency of muscular patterning and the temporal and spatial phasic relationship between participating muscles during performance or learning.

As movements become more and more complex, the number of linkages increases and the total number of degrees of freedom of movement used may also increase. A specific number of degrees of freedom of movement are available between each link, and each link has mass, moment of inertia, length, and a unique set of movement directions. Within a particular kinematic chain of movement, as the number of participating links increases so does the total number of degrees of freedom of movement for the chain. For example, the relatively simple task of throwing a ball involves regulating 17 degrees of freedom in the kinematic chain described by the articulations from the shoulder girdle to the fingers. This complexity obviously increases manifestly when, for example, the performer is running. Depending upon the activity, however, only a portion of the available degrees within the chain are usually made use of. This figure of 17 degrees of freedom does not account for movement that also occurs in other articulations and between other participating links, such as the knee, hip, and spine. Furthermore, there is the important aspect of reducing or decreasing the degrees of freedom through improved joint stabilization and muscular control. It is easy to see, therefore, that as the number of participating links increases the degrees of freedom of movement increases and the process of regulation and coordination of the movement becomes increasingly complex. This speaks most directly to the notion of links and as yet says little about information processing and perceptual processes so important in regulation of movement.

When we speak of coordination as being the mastery of "redundant degrees of freedom of movement within a kinematic chain of movement," we mean that all possible directions of movement within a chain have to be controlled or regulated. Some of the redundant degrees of freedom of movement available are controlled through fixation types of movement, others by acceleration or deceleration movements, and still others through lengthening contraction. The potential muscular forces available across a particular articulation are either inhibited or facilitated to bring about the necessary control; that is, the *muscular forces are modulated for a particular action* in order to bring about the required movement.

As regulatory control of the movement improves the structural components of the muscular forces will become increasingly coordinated. These structural components include the displacement, velocity, acceleration, and force generated for each link participating in each movement. For example, during early stages of skill acquisition the nature and pattern of the movement within a particular chain of movement is usually constrained, stiff, and variable. Through practice of the skill, the movement appears to exhibit a freer, less constrained, and more consistent pattern. In addition to smoother movement parameters there is usually an associated improvement in degree of goal and accomplishment. As growth and development occurs concomitant selective loosening and increased segmental control are observed. In other words, both experience and growth and development play an important part in the observed changes in control of the degrees of freedom of movement.

When learning a new task the central nervous system (CNS) is initially unable to deal with the abundance of degrees of freedom of movement available. Hence we observe the jerky, inconsistent movement early in learning a skill, as well as early in life. Coordination improves as the degrees of freedom are clarified and selectively modulated and decreased. From the point of view of the CNS this involves a kind of selective inhibition or selective disinhibition of movements in order to control the degrees of freedom of movement. These changes are often obvious through the eye of the trained teacher. The changes may be reflected in overall smoothness of the movement, as well as in improved performance scores and related consistency or reduction of variability in performance. The reader should realize that for any desired movement, for example shooting a free throw in basketball, the variety of muscular activity and individual muscles participating is quite large. On the other hand the degrees of freedom to be controlled for the task is more easily specified and can be reduced to a small and controllable number of parameters and variables. It is the control through higher-level organization that allows the ultimate coordination of all participating links into a smooth, effective movement for projecting a basketball accurately through the hoop. The central nervous system will not specify muscles and level of muscular activity needed in a particular task; rather it is the resultant integration of peripheral information (the ongoing state of the organism with reference to position, tension, speed, etc.) with the intention of the action (a CNS function) that determine the outcome.

Finally, it can be stated that coordination guarantees that the movement (direct adaptive and goal-directed) will exhibit homogeneity, integration, and structural unity (Bernstein, 1967:30). Homogeneity insures that the parts making up a movement have little variation over trials; there is a more or less uniform structure throughout, and elements composing the movement are not discoordinate or dissimilar. For all segments involved in a particular task, the various movement parameters will demonstrate a degree of consistency. A decreased variation between the parts comprising the movement will be observed. The elements making up the movement will be similar, not discoordinate. *Integration* combines the parts or elements into a whole, integrating CNS processes of sensory perception, memory, information processing, and effector mechanisms with the morphology (or state of the organism) and environment. Integration insures the complete and unified movement. *Structural unity* is the interrelation of different units within the hierarchical organization of the nervous system (Higgins, 1972). By this we mean that the hierarchical organizational properties of the CNS must be reflected in the structure of the observed movement. Coordinated movement, conditioned by the constraints of morphology, biomechanics, and environment and resultant homogeneity, integration, and structural unity, thus dictates the dynamic features of our skilled movements.

A neural message arising from higher CNS centers and directed toward completing some form of action or movement must adapt to both the internal and the external forces within the system. That is, movement of our links is not under the passive control of the CNS but is shaped as a result of the interaction between external forces, internal conditions, and the neural impulse itself. It is the integration of these forces, conditions, and neural impulses that accounts for coordinated movements.

Presently we know relatively little about the relationship between the neural impulse and the resultant movement. Considerable work is now going forward that is looking at the problem of organization and control of movement. This work is of particular relevance here and involves crossing several disciplines and modes of inquiry—neurophysiology, psychology, engineering, computer science, and biology, to name but a few (Gelfand, 1971). This is an area needing much attention before we are fully to appreciate and understand the organization schema for regulation and control of our movements. We do know that as the complexity of the kinematic chain increases for a given movement, the one-to-one relationship between the neural impulse and the movement will decrease (Bernstein, 1967). This may imply a shift in levels of control where as movements become more and more coordinated and more autonomous, their regulation shifts to lower levels for final ultimate control. External information is important in the control and regulation of our movements. As the environment may be moving in time and space, for example, the CNS is responsible for processing sensory information derived from the external world and the internal state of the participating limbs and body. This processed sensory information is then translated through both higher- and lower-level integration into appropriate actions through the neural impulse directed at contraction of appropriate muscles or muscle groups.[1]

For any coordinated movement there is a gradual and even flow of action or activity from one muscle or group of muscles to another. At a behavioral level we observe actions that are similar, but the muscular activity itself will be different. This difference is dependent upon the external and internal condition. Behaviorally our concerns are therefore more directly related to actions than they are to muscles. What we should be observing and studying is the actions being performed, not necessarily the individual muscular contractions.

Sensory feedback provides the CNS with information used to make adjustments in the centrally represented plans for action—*motor plans.* These motor plans are thought to be represented as hierarchically arranged sequences of operations within the cerebral cortex and are further represented as actions and not as specific muscles (Higgins, 1972; Miller et al., 1960; Pribram, 1972).

PATTERNS OF MOVEMENT

The regulation and control of coordinated movement is achieved through a self-regulating system, a closed circle of interaction between internal processes and external, or environmental, conditions. In this chapter we are primarily interested in the product, the final outcome, of the self-regulating system: the movement itself. We now know what a coordinated act is, and we need to additionally identify and understand the composition of the movement, the structure of the movement.

The study of patterns of movement is the study of the movements themselves. A *pattern of movement* is a complex whole, characterized by a definite arrangement of interrelated muscular actions directed toward accomplishment of a goal. Patterns of movement are sequences of integrated and coordinated muscular activity that produce overt behavior in the form of body and limb movement—body transport and limb manipulation. A pattern of movement will indicate a change in body or limb position in time and space. It is the result of forces generated within the moving system or of external forces imposed upon the organism or both. *The pattern of the movement is the structure of the movement.* Patterns of movement are acquired as a result of practice according to the environmental regulation provided by the goal. Every pattern of movement is organized in time and space and yields some kind of behavioral output in the form of displacement, velocity, acceleration, and force. Patterns of movement within a self-regulating system are thought to be regulated and controlled by environmental, biomechanical, and morphologic constraints.

Observation and measurement of patterns of movement provide means by which we can determine the nature of the spatial and temporal components of a particular movement, of a series of movements, or of a portion of a movement. Several possible outcomes of such analysis result in the determination of (1) the phasic relationship[2] between participating segments in terms of time and space, (2) the changes occurring between and within movement phases with practice, (3) the relationship between parameters of the movement and morphologic, biomechanical, and environmental conditions.

Patterns of movement are the end product of the organism's ability to react to three peripheral sources of variation: (1) mechanical sources, (2) complexity of the kinematic chain, and (3) moment-to-moment condition of the organism and the environment (Bernstein, 1967). The *mechanical source* of variation results from the effects of physical factors such as muscular tension and force, mass, inertia, center of gravity, and translation of angular momentum or movement to linear movement. The source of variation provided by the *complexity of the kinematic chain* relates to degrees of freedom of movement and number of segments involved in a particular movement. The *moment-to-moment condition of the organism and the environment* produces a very complex source of variation related to the process of information feedback and effector processes. That is, the sensory relationship between the moving segments or efference and incoming environmental or afferent information is itself a source of variation that must be contended with to produce coordinated, organized movement.

Fig. 3-1 represents an example of a pattern of movement recorded for a 4-year-old boy by the use of cinematographic techniques.[3] The child was filmed throwing a ball with (Fig. 3-1, *A*) and without (Fig. 3-1, *B*) a target. Since the activity was filmed in a laboratory setting, body transport was controlled by asking the child to throw from behind a line and without walking or running forward. The displacement (*x-y* coordinate points)

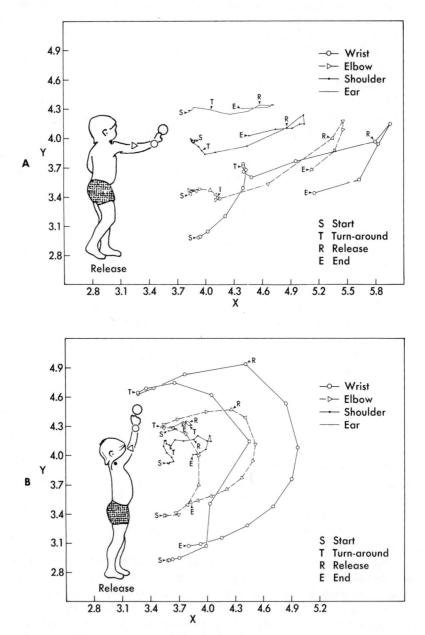

Fig. 3-1. Pattern of movement of 4-year-old boy throwing ball. **A,** With target. **B,** Without target.

of the ear, shoulder, elbow, and wrist were recorded in order to demonstrate one example of pattern of movement. The reader should note that there is a decided difference between the two patterns depicted that can be attributed to the use of a target in one case and no target in the other. Furthermore, if we were to record several trials under such condition we would also see condition differences that could be attributed to the notion of inconsistent pattern of movement during early stages of learning.

The patterns shown in Fig. 3-1 also show three important points within the movement. The release point (R), the point at which the ball is released, serves as the first point for analysis. All subsequent points are obtained in relation to this point. The turn-around point (T) is the point where the movement of the wrist is clearly in the direction of the target or throwing area. Between T and R is what we might call the action phase of the movement. The starting point (S) of the movement represents the point at which the throwing task begins. The area between S and T is called the preparatory phase. The follow-through obviously comes after R and is represented by the lines following that point.

These patterns are intended to provide the reader with an example of a pattern of movement. In this case the pattern of movement is for displacement of specific anatomic points as they move through space and time during the course of throwing a ball. A pattern of movement might also be represented through velocity or acceleration measures, by angular measures between segments, or by force parameters. The measurement technique should be chosen for its appropriateness to the research or observational question asked. In the example we chose displacement because this technique represents the movement of points through space and time and depicts the relationship between them in relation to two environmental conditions.

Differentiation of patterns of movement

As we observe, study, and analyze patterns of movement for a particular skill over the course of practice, we note that certain changes in the patterns appear to take place. It is the modification of patterns of movements with practice that we call the *differentiation of patterns of movement*. We have observed that patterns of movement appear to change in different ways for the same task when the task is performed under different environmental conditions (Higgins and Spaeth, 1972). Differentiation of movement is the change in the pattern of movement resulting from practice under similar or differing environmental conditions. The patterns of movement, though perhaps of the same class or task, are modified in specific ways, leading to particular functional relationships. The differentiation of patterns of movement is the result of practice, environmental conditions, and task specifics.

For example, were a student to learn to hit a baseball from a batting

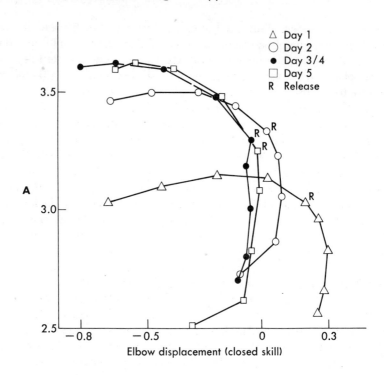

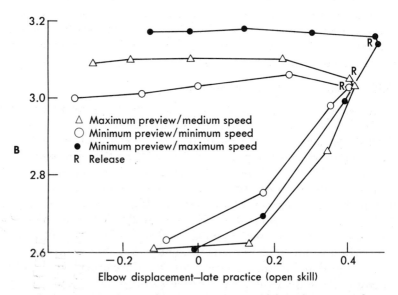

Fig. 3-2. Pattern of elbow movement of 11-year-old boy throwing a dart. **A,** Stationary target. **B,** Moving target. (From Higgins and Spaeth, 1972.)

tee, we would observe that the pattern of movement, the swing, would become very consistent with practice. If the position of the ball were changed the batter would then, with practice, develop an additional pattern of movement for that spatial location of the ball, that is, the pattern of movement for the swing would have differentiated into two distinct patterns of movement for hitting the baseball from two batting tee positions.

If we now expect our student batter to hit a pitched ball, we will observe that the two differentiated patterns for hitting a ball off the tee are completely ineffective. The condition of the environment has now changed from a stationary environment to a moving environment. The two differentiated patterns are not effective for the condition of spatial and temporal environmental change. The batter now has to contend with a ball moving at varying speeds along varying trajectories. This produces an entirely different set of conditions against which his movements have to be produced. Had the student initially been introduced to the pitched ball his patterns of movements would have differentiated according to the population of possible spatial and temporal conditions existing in the real world of hitting a baseball—for each speed and each trajectory a specific but related pattern of movement would have been developed.

This notion is demonstrated in Fig. 3-2 where an 11-year-old boy's pattern of movement is depicted for a dart throw at a stationary and a moving target. Note that there is a difference in the overall time taken to complete the movement (as seen by the decreased distance moved and fewer number of frames between the beginning of the movement and the release). In addition, the point of release is different, and the angle of movement for the elbow between the beginning of the movement and the release is different for each condition.

Research has demonstrated that a learner's movements will differentiate in relation to the condition of the environment (Higgins and Spaeth, 1972). Fig. 3-3 is a schematic diagram of this notion. For a task performed in a stable environment (stationary target), there is a reduction in the amount of variability of pattern of movement over practice. The subject's pattern of movement differentiates toward a consistent, relatively similar pattern of movement. When a similar task is performed in an environment where the spatial and temporal conditions are changing (a moving target), we see that the patterns of movement differentiate in accordance with the specific condition of the environment (speed and location of the target).

Analysis reveals that movements are extremely fluid within a particular pattern and for a specific environmental condition. The organization of movement is dependent upon the initial and ongoing position of the participating segments, the nature of the resistive forces, individual morphology, biomechanical factors, and the environment. The same

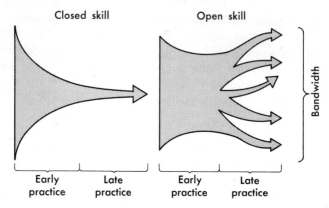

Fig. 3-3. Schematic representation of differentiation of pattern of movement. (From Higgins and Spaeth, 1972.)

movement result can be obtained in a variety of ways. Movements are never reproduced identically; it is merely the variability within a bandwidth of a pattern of movement that may be reproducible. There are too many intervening factors for absolute, one-to-one, identical reproduction of patterns of movement to occur.

A bandwidth for a pattern of movement is defined as corresponding to the overall schema for organization of movement for a particular condition. The condition is related to the nature of environmental, biomechanical, and morphologic constraints imposed on the organization of the movement system.

The organization of skilled coordinated movement involves the resolution of the constant imposition of environmental, biomechanical, and morphologic constraints. Our organized, coordinated, skilled movements are the behavioral outcome of the complex process of resolving these constraints.

NOTES

1. Higher and lower levels of integration imply that there is a hierarchical organization for movement control and regulation. From higher levels may come some general plan for action with the finer and final parameters of the movement decided through lower level integrative processes (perhaps at the level of the spinal cord). At the lower level there would be a tuning or preparatory state set by the higher centers integrated with peripheral input derived from the moment-to-moment state of the links and the environment.
2. Phasic relationship refers to the observation and measurement of two or more limb segments or participating muscles for any given point in time or for a particular point in a movement.
3. The patterns of movement in Fig. 3-1 are part of a film analysis project in motor development at Teachers College, Columbia University.

FOUR

Levels of analysis: a model approach

The systematic analysis of any motor act must first involve a theoretical base and a carefully defined rationale out of which relevant questions can be formulated. Up to this point an overview has been provided concerning the underlying theoretical formulations related to the classification of movement and the regulation and control of voluntary human movement. This chapter outlines a model for the systematic study of human movement whose central focus incorporates four levels of analysis (Fig. 4-1). The *levels of analysis* have meaning when selection of an appropriate classification system is viewed in conjunction with the constraints imposed upon the movement. Once this conjunction is understood we can support the feasibility of a multidimensional analytic approach, an approach that affords us the opportunity to more effectively identify and analyze the structural elements of movements and the underlying schema for the organization of movement.

Fig. 4-1 shows the overall schema and interrelatedness of the identified components prior to the analysis of the organization of movement. The schema represents a cyclic approach involving the elements the system must organize and regulate (constraints), the choice of a movement classification system, and the levels through which these elements can be analyzed. The *taxonomy of movement* is included in this model since the choice of a system used to classify movement has a direct relationship to the level and nature of analysis undertaken. The box to the right of "taxonomy" simply illustrates the system of closed and open skills described in Chapter Two, which may be appropriate for some forms of analysis. Along with the theoretical base, taxonomy is one of the analytic factors contributing to the kind of question asked. Once the question is identified, an appropriate level of analysis is selected; dependent upon

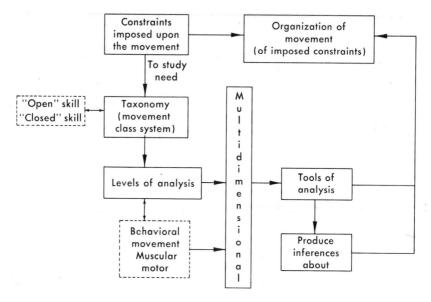

Fig. 4-1. Flow diagram of the systematic study of biomechanics and skill acquisition.

the level selected, appropriate tools for measurement and recording movement, either qualitative or quantitative, are chosen and provide the information within the framework of the questions asked. Inferences can then be drawn regarding the organization of the movement.

This chapter begins by discussing the organization of movement as the central focus for movement analysis. A brief explication of the imposed constraints, which are a primary factor in organization of movement, leads to a methodologic focus dealing with levels of analysis. The multidimensional analytic approach is an outgrowth and serves as a natural bridge for the discussion in Chapter Nine related to tools of analysis and is an important concept for analysis of human movement.

ORGANIZATION OF MOVEMENT

Organization of movement is a purposive, systematic arrangement of the parts—the *structural elements of the movement*—comprising any action within a vast array of goal-directed responses; it is the systematic manner in which the organism produces goal-directed movement. The structural elements comprising a movement are the related displacement, velocity, and acceleration characteristics determining the pattern of the movement. These elements can be measured by the researcher or are determined through qualitative observational analysis. Very often, and especially in observational work, what is measured or observed is usually a derivative or abstraction of one or more of these elements. In Chapter Nine we will see that the derivatives or abstractions of the elements make up the critical factors of a movement, the essential features and factors that must be a part of the movement and in fact may ultimately be the least modifiable aspect of the movement. Displacement, velocity, and acceleration can be represented by spatial and temporal relationships; hence, *the organization of movement is represented by the functional relationship between the spatial and temporal components of any purposeful, volitional, goal-directed pattern of movement.* Through careful analysis of the structural elements of movement, these relationships can be established and a view of how our movements are organized begins to emerge. That is, understanding the movement aids in understanding the underlying organizational processes (Gelfand, 1971; Gentile et al., 1975).

Goal-directed movements are considered the end product of a complexly organized and hierarchically arranged schema resulting in skilled, coordinated movement. Movements can be both means and ends; they are both process and product. It may be that two systems are operating, one a process responsible for transforming the environment (Gentile and Nacson, 1976). The goal of the movement can be either the movement itself or effectuating a change in the environment. In either circumstance, the process responsible for the required pattern of movement must account for a number of sources of variation. As teachers, we are most accustomed to observing the product; the product is the environmental change brought about by the movement itself—doing something to the environment. This is in contrast to expressive dance or nonverbal communication and sports activities where the movement itself is the goal of the activity.

As the organization of movement develops—and it develops within a context of acquisition of skill and through growth and development—small and simple actions are increasingly welded together to permit larger and more complex actions to occur. Associations between these actions form what we observe as behavioral outcomes in skilled movement. The potentially independent actions are "welded into one coherent sequence" (Lorenz, 1969).

CONSTRAINTS IMPOSED UPON MOVEMENT

Organized movements depend upon the system's ability to deal with three sources of variation. These sources of variation are a form of constraint, each of which is imposed upon the organization of the movement. Each variation is in some way balanced or compensated for by the various levels of control operating within the system. Each potential source of

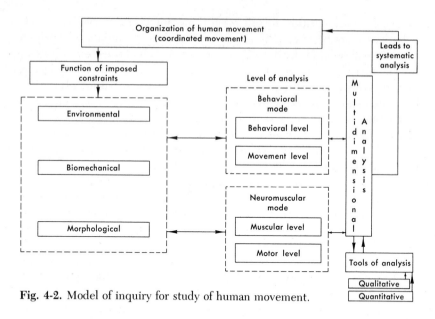

Fig. 4-2. Model of inquiry for study of human movement.

variation must be overcome as part of the process for organizing and producing our movements.

Three constraints derived from these sources of variation, identified in Fig. 4-2, are environmental, biomechanical, and morphologic.

As will be seen, these constraints are logically related to the levels of analysis, thus providing a major element in the model for the understanding and systematic study of human movement (Fig. 4-2). (A constraint is the act of confining or constraining, and for our purposes means the confinement and restraining of input and output derived from various levels of system operation so as to produce order in the resulting movement.) Coordinated movements are possible because of the predictability associated with specific features within the three indentified constraints. These predictable features or redundancies set a limit to chaos, and in that sense are constraints; they are also constraints in the sense that, unless behavior is conditioned by them, it will be nonadaptive (Howard and Templeton, 1966). Our movements are developed and maintained through a highly complex, self-regulating system that is continuously molded and conditioned by the spatial and temporal characteristics inherent in the physical world (environmental and biomechanical constraints) and in the organism itself (morphologic constraints). The dotted lines surrounding environmental, biomechanical, and morphologic constraints in Fig. 4-2 illustrate the interrelationship between the environmental, biomechanical, and morphologic constraints. It is only through careful and thoughtful reflection and research that we can come fully to appreciate the range and specific effect of these relationships.

Environmental constraints

Environmental constraints relate to the spatial and temporal configuration of events in the world external to the organism. The spatial and temporal configuration of the environment places one source of variation upon the organism. If the desired control and effectiveness for goal accomplishment are to be produced, these variations must be matched by the movement. In this context the environment is viewed as a continuum of spatial and temporal control along which the predictability of events varies from certain to uncertain. Hence the continuum ranges from an environment having an associated high degree of predictability against which to match movements (environmental certainty) to an environment having relatively little associated predictability against which to match movements (environmental uncertainty). Environments with high degrees of predictability are spatially and temporally certain; movements must thereby match the spatial characteristics of the environment (e.g., hitting a golf ball or performing a gymnastic stunt). At the other end of the continuum the environment is spatially and temporally uncertain, and thus the degree to which prediction about the spatial and temporal events can be made is decreased (e.g., hitting a baseball or catching a pass in football). Skills performed within environments of spatial and temporal certainty have been referred to as closed skills; those performed within uncertain environmental conditions have been referred to as open skills.

In the sports skills setting, rules for performance and equipment design and characteristics are also considered environmental constraints (Fig. 4-2). Rules and equipment impose a much more invariant or deterministic form of constraint upon the movement. From the performance viewpoint they are invariant, unchanging; nevertheless, the performance must meet or match characteristics of each to achieve an effective, efficient performance outcome.

Biomechanical constraints

The biomechanical constraints relate to physical laws and principles that for a specific task or skill can dictate an optimum theoretical way that the movement should be approached. Biomechanical constraints relate to the organism's ability to deal with independent forces such as gravity, mass, and inertia (the peripheral, mechanical source of variation affecting movement, described in Chapter Three). The laws of physics will dictate certain invariant properties that the performer must match or accommodate in his movement. The principles related to the effect of gravity are a common example. All our movements are in some way affected by gravity. The laws of aerodynamics and hydrodynamics also impose constraints upon the organization of movement. It is the identification and separation of specific properties and factors inherent in these laws that allow us better to understand the determinants and the indeterminants that result in controlled movement. For example, in Chapter Seven when we discuss critical features of the movement as an important aspect of observation for teachers, questions to ask include the following: What physical laws or principles impose determinant and indeterminant constraints upon the movement? What is the relationship between the indeterminant constraints and the invariant-variant properties or features of the movement?

Morphologic constraints

Morphologic constraints are factors that relate to the overall structure and form of the organism and the relationship between structure and function. These constraints include such anatomic factors as skeletal arrangement, articular structure and its resultant action, anatomic location of muscles, and type of muscle and its resultant action. In addition to these specific anatomic considerations, morphologic constraints are also related to such perceptual processes as sensory detection-processing system, pattern recognition, decision-making, and memory.

Organismic variables are also included under morphologic constraints. The physical size and shape of a performer, among other factors, have a direct relationship to the nature of the movement produced (pattern of movement) for any task or skill. For example, when diving, the large heavy-set performer will have a different type of morphologic constraint problem to overcome than will the short, wiry performer. Age, sex, height and weight, and experience are organismic variables that affect organization of movement as morphologic constraints.

Summarizing this section on the constraints imposed upon the movement, a moderate degree of speculation is necessary. Study of the expanded model (Fig. 4-2) indicates the existence of an interface (two-way arrows) between the constraints and the levels of analysis. The interface relates to what may be viewed in the patterns of movement. That is, given each constraint, what can we speculate as to the influence upon the pattern of movement? The observation and identification of differentiation of the patterns, their similarities, and their uniqueness are the basic means by which the imposition of constraints may be evaluated. This evaluation is best achieved through one or more levels of analysis, each of which provides a specific type of information.

The influence of environmental variation is largely a result of the performer's ability to make predictions about the immediate future regarding the spatial and temporal conditions of the environment. Organizationally, the movement characteristics then develop specific spatial and temporal components that for each performer are related to the spatial and temporal condition of the environment. The spatial component of the movement relates to displacement of a limb segment or of the body; the temporal component of the movement relates to the timing, speed, and acceleration of the limb segment or body. Hence we might suggest that the observed patterns of movement will differentiate spatially and temporally according to the regulatory demands of the environment (Higgins and Spaeth, 1972; Spaeth, 1973).

On the other hand, the biomechanical constraints may provide a degree of similarity between performers' patterns of movement. This similarity between and within performers' patterns of movement is in part related to the predictability of the physical laws imposing themselves on all movement. The environmental constraints are by degree less predictable than are the biomechanical constraints. Since the biomechanical constructs (physical laws and principles) remain constant, the resultant pattern of movement may be similar from performer to performer on a given task, except as influenced by variables from the environment and the morphology. If it were possible experimentally to hold the variables of environmental and morphologic constraints constant, then we might observe greater similarity between individual performers' patterns of movement for a specific task or skill.

Morphology accounts for considerable variation in our movements. What is interesting to note here is that in terms of performance the patterns of movement observed are in all cases unique to the individual performer. The uniqueness of these patterns from one performer to another is in major part due to differences in morphology. Assuming that both environmental and biomechanical sources of variation are relatively constant, for any performance the patterns of movement will ultimately be unique to that performer. In other words, the construction of our bones, joints, and muscles are unique for each of us. Obviously this unique structure will determine to some extent how our movements look: the tall, lanky performer will exhibit a very different pattern of movement in hitting a baseball than will the short, stocky performer. In both cases some of the similarity between the performers might be accounted for by both environmental and biomechanical constraints that are the same for both.

Of the three sources of variation, the environmental constraints will produce the highest degree of variation in pattern of movement within performers (Gentile et al., 1975). These patterns of movement reflect the uniqueness and variation inherent in the spatial and temporal properites of the environment. From what we know at present it is the demands of the environment that most affect our performance, that impose the most pervasive demand that the system must match in organized movement. Though for each performer these constraints may become very predictable, and in fact probably do as skill improves, they also produce wide variation between individuals because of the wide range of individual differences.

There is obviously a constant interaction between the three described constraints. Their interaction and regulation is what produces organized, coordinated movement (Figs. 4-1 and 4-2). It may be that experimentally manipulating aspects of one constraint (source of variation) while keeping the other two constant will produce valuable insight into how we move and learn to move. Dependent upon the taxonomy and level of analysis chosen, the contribution of each constraint to the organization of the movement can be determined.

LEVELS OF ANALYSIS

To begin with, two segments are arbitrarily formulated within which two levels of analysis are contained (Fig. 4-2). This was done to clarify the analytic approach and to emphasize the convenient dichotomy produced by the skin. The *behavioral mode* contains the two levels of analysis, behavioral and movement, for events occurring "outside the skin." The *neuromuscular mode* contains the two levels of analysis, muscular and motor, for events occurring "inside the skin." The types and tools of observation used for each level will be discussed more fully in Chapter Nine (see Table 5).

Behavioral mode

The behavioral mode is composed of the two levels of analysis: behavioral and movement.

The behavioral level of analysis essentially views the outcome of the movement in terms of its consequence, efficiency, and effectiveness of goal accomplishment. Within this level our interest is in performance scores over time, consistency of these scores (variability), and effectiveness of the produced outcome. The best single measure of level of skill is the "range of consistency" of goal attainment (Bartlett, 1947a and b). The behavioral level, therefore, is primarily concerned with this range of consistency and the relationship of this type of outcome measure to each of the remaining levels of analysis.

The *movement level of analysis* is used to study the observable behavioral responses that result in the displacement of one or more limb segments or the body. At this level three factors are observed and measured: kinematic, kinetic, and kinesic. The kinematic factor deals with the consistency of the kinematic elements of the movement: displacement, velocity, and acceleration. The kinetic factor deals with the consistency level and type of force production, and problems where analysis of center of gravity changes are observed or measured; that is, the analysis of patterns of movement as kinetic factors. The kinesic factor relates to observations made of nonverbal communicative behavior. This is a large, rapidly expanding area of study and will be dealt with only by way of suggesting that the contribution of the general field of biomechanics and movement analysis to kinesics can be most important. Within the sport skill setting, there is a need to use biomechanical tools to investigate the nonverbal communication elements that may play an important role in teacher behavior and player-player interaction. Kinesic analysis of movement has been used to study dance movements in a cross-cultural perspective, as well as communicative movements in human interactions (Birdwhistle, 1970; Lomax et al., 1969). It is largely observational and thus is a qualitative tool of analysis.

The critical element here, as with the behavioral level, is consistency of patterns of movement, whether viewed as kinematic, kinetic, or kinesic. On the other hand, when simply observing the movement and not engaging in measurement, this level represents a subjective-descriptive analysis of the essential components making up the movement.

Neuromuscular mode

The neuromuscular mode is composed of two levels of analysis: muscular and motor.

The *muscular level of analysis* designates those "responses occurring within the contractible elements of the system"—the muscles themselves (Higgins, 1972). Within this level of analysis several types of observations can be made: (1) muscle function analysis for any particular skill performance or task, (2) relationship between specific muscles and muscle groups and the active skeletal system, (3) phasic relationship between muscles participating in a specific task, (4) the magnitude and duration of muscular activity as a function of task and level of skill, and (5) change occurring during acquisition of skill, involving any of the types of observation stated above. This is an important level of analysis because it represents a means for peripherally observing the signals being transmitted from the CNS to the muscles that produce the response. Commonly these observations are made with the use of electromyographic techniques.

The *motor level of analysis* designates the internal activity or events related to sensory-motor input and output functions of the CNS. Only in recent years has technology made it feasible to analyze neurophysiologic function in the intact human organism. With this added level of analysis, investigators are now in a position to study motoric behavior in humans (Vaughan and Ritter, 1973; Walter, 1954).

MULTIDIMENSIONAL ANALYSIS OF SKILL

Too often teachers and researchers in motor skill and performance view skill in terms of the behavioral outcomes or the movement produced, usually for a single trial. More often than not, these observations are for a particular level of skill, or at best compare one level of skill with another level of skill. For the teacher, very often a high level of skilled performance serves as the model for teaching at the beginning levels of skill. A student may be observed shooting a jump shot in basketball and if a basket is scored, we assume the movements to be correct, perhaps rightfully so since the goal was achieved; if the basket is missed, we assume the movements to be incorrect. Very often the relationship between the movement producing the shot and the behavioral outcome is not analyzed. More importantly we are usually unaware of the progressive changes in the structure of the movement (movement parameters) and the behavioral outcomes (score) over time. A multidimensional approach will aid the teacher and researcher in observing and measuring the progressive component changes occurring during acquisition of skill and performance.

There are many ways in which a specific task or skill can be performed. Looking at the variation or consistency of performance scores for and between individual performers tells us little more than that something is happening; this orientation does not help us understand the underlying organizational schema of the movement. Identification of the effect of the constraints imposing themselves upon the ultimate organization and control of the movement may be a more fruitful way to resolve the important question of the relationship between what produced the movement and its ultimate behavioral outcome. It is therefore important to look not only at the outcome measure, as indicated by overall achievement, but also at the "manner in which it was attained" (Welford, 1968). Welford (1968) and others (Fitts, 1964; Kay, 1969, 1971) have pointed out that performance cannot be adequately investigated in terms of discreet, isolated reactions. Instead we need to investigate the details and progressive changes of the skill or task as a whole, throughout the entire ergonomic cycle, over time, and from multiple observational levels of analysis. Thus, within the context of acquisition of skill and skilled performance we have a case for the multidimensional analysis of human movement.

The *multidimensional analysis of human movement* is thus conceived as the simultaneous observation or measurement of two or more movement parameters or levels of analysis in our model (Fig. 4-2). These observations or measurements are most useful when viewed over the course of acquiring a skill. Under what conditions do changes in patterns of movement occur? How does "the role of the limbs and body progressively" change during the acquisition of skill (Kay, 1969, 1971)?

Multidimensional analysis juxtaposes measures or observations from one or more levels of analysis. For example, while varying the environmental condition we can compare the behavioral level (performance outcomes over time) with the movement level (progressive changes in the movement) (Higgins and Spaeth, 1972). Furthermore, comparing progressive changes occuring at the muscular level with progressive changes at the movement level is still another broad approach leading to the understanding of organization of movement and performance. Study of the

> structure of the movement multidimensionally entails the identification of both the characteristics of the movement produced *and* the underlying process of organization of the movement. The structure is the integral formation of the movement: that which constitutes the movement displacements involved, and the forces involved. (Higgins, 1972.)

When two or more levels of analysis are juxtaposed in an analytic schema (e.g., behavioral outcomes with movement parameters), information is derived that is related to the relationship between the character of the movement and the performance outcomes. That is, we can obtain information and establish relationships along the following lines: (1) consistency and change in goal attainment, (2) consistency and change in pattern of movement, (3) consistency and change in pattern of muscular activity, and (4) consistency and change in neurologic activity.

The manner in which this multidimensional approach can function can be briefly outlined by two examples. The first example has been the approach taken in the Motor Learning Laboratory, Teachers College, Columbia University, and involves using the environmental constraints as the independent variable (Higgins and Spaeth, 1972; Spaeth, 1973). The second example is speculative, though not without a theoretical base, and involves using the morphologic constraint as the independent variable. The environmental conditions are manipulated in the first example, and organismic variables are manipulated in the second example. In both examples, the underlying theme is the investigation of the nature of movement organization occurring during the acquisition of a motor skill within variable constraint contexts. The purpose of these examples is to illustrate a process-oriented approach, and hence data obtained and the findings will be limited to a short summary.

Example one: behavioral level and movement level of analysis in relation to environmental condition

The basic question has been what effect the spatial and temporal condition of the environment has upon the performance scores and movement parameter. The first stage in answering this question was to decide how to manipulate the environmental variable. A taxonomy was selected that divides the condition of the environment in such a fashion as to place tasks or skills in two broad categories: open skills and closed skills (Gentile, 1972; Gentile, Higgins, Miller, and Rosen, 1975). A task—dart throwing—was then selected because the condition of the environment could be manipulated in such a way that the task could be classified as either an open or a closed skill dependent upon whether a spatially-temporally certain environment or a spatially-temporally uncertain environment was chosen.

The second stage involved determining the level of analysis. The behavioral and movement levels were selected as the dependent variable. Within the multidimensional analytic approach we selected the behavioral mode—behavioral and movement levels—since we were interested in changes in score and movement during practice on a dart-throwing task.

The third stage involved selection of tools for analysis. For us, the most appropriate tools for the questions asked were within the quantitative domain. This entailed cinematography and performance scores for the dart throwing task.

The fourth stage was the collection and analysis of data.

The analysis of data naturally leads to interpretation of results, which of course comprised the fifth stage. Here we were able to draw inferences about the nature of the organization of movement. If we had not used the two levels of analysis from the behavioral mode, our inferences and conclusions would not be as strongly supported as we think they are.

So that the reader is provided with a sense of closure, following are the kinds of inferences and conclusions that to date can be drawn from this work:

1. A high degree of both spatial and temporal consistency in the pattern of movement is observed for a highly trained subject performing a closed type skill—the cartwheel (Higgins, 1970a).
2. For a closed type skill—the standing broad jump—increased consistency in the temporal components of a movement and for selected spatial components of a movement occur as a result of practice (eighty trials) (Hoffman, 1971).
3. For a closed type skill, the consistency of the pattern of movement appears to have a direct relationship with consistency of performance outcomes (scores) (Higgins and Spaeth, 1972).
4. For an open type skill—dart throwing—the pattern of movement emerging as a result of practice is related to the specific spatial-temporal configuration of the environment; several distinct patterns of movement emerged as a function of the position and speed of the moving target (Higgins and Spaeth, 1972).

Example two: behavioral and muscular levels of analysis in relation to morphologic constraints (organismic variable of sex)

The basic question in this example might be the following: What effect do sex differences have upon the performance scores and movement parameters during acquisition of a skill? The same process can be followed as outlined in example one. Stage one determines the independent variable, sex. We might choose to use a closed type skill. Stage two selects a task whereby both behavioral measures (performance scores) and muscular information can be obtained (electromyography). Stage three selects a performance score and electromyographic technique appropriate to the task. We might, therefore, be interested in changes in performance scores and their relationship to changes in the phasic relationship between selected muscle groups. In stage four we collect our data, and in stage five we analyze the data and draw our inferences about the observed sex differences in score and patterning of muscular activity during the acquisition of a specific skill.

· · ·

In both examples the emphasis is upon a process-oriented approach where we begin with a broad conceptual picture of the world out of which we ask our questions. Each question and subsequent answer can then be fed back into the model, the model can be reevaluated, and subsequent questions asked.

Within each level of the analytic model, the identification of the detailed and progressive changes leads logically to our understanding of the organization and control of human movement. Multidimensional analysis aids in establishing the relationship between levels and constraints. As these relationships are established we will find that our understanding of skilled human movement will increase and that as teachers our ability to make decisions for structuring the learning environment and facilitating acquisition of skill will also improve.

FIVE

Neurophysiology and human movement

Ultimately the functional responsibility of our nervous system is to provide us with an awareness of the environment in which we move and an awareness of the sensations arising from within the body as we move. Given this information, the nervous system can provide the necessary regulation and volitional control of our skeletal-muscular actions and reflex responses, and involuntary regulation of our vital organs and their functions. This chapter focuses on voluntary, goal-directed, adaptive moments. Reflexive responses are discussed only in relation to this focus.

In order to perform these varied and important tasks, the nervous system is intricately organized as a hierarchy of many closely coordinated centers, each having its own particular role. Each of these nervous centers is under the controlling influence of higher centers, which in turn are regulated by still higher centers, until finally the level of the *cerebral cortex* is reached.

The pathways for communication between the different centers are numerous, and their connections are complicated and incompletely understood. Moreover, little is known as yet concerning why and how some of the more complex nervous functions are carried out.

Any study of the neurophysiology of human movement must be made with these complexities, uncertainties, and limitations of knowledge in mind. We shall omit certain details related to structure and frequently simplify discussion to considerations of nervous system functions. Every attempt is made, however, to present the fundamental concepts of

54

neurophysiology as they relate to the study of the organization of human movement behavior.

BASIC ORGANIZATION OF THE NERVOUS SYSTEM

For convenience in study, the nervous system can be divided into two parts: the central nervous system and the peripheral nervous system. The central nervous system (CNS) consists of the brain and spinal cord; the peripheral nervous system (PNS) consists of the cranial and spinal nerves and the peripheral portions of the autonomic nervous system. (We will not be discussing the autonomic nervous system).

Central nervous system

The major parts of the *brain* include the cerebral hemispheres, the cerebellar hemispheres, and the brain stem. The cerebral and cerebellar hemispheres are intimately attached to a central stalklike structure called the brain stem. The uppermost part of the brain stem is the diencephalon, with which the cerebral hemispheres are connected and through which they communicate with lower levels of the brain stem and the spinal cord. Below the diencephalon (in inferior order) the brain stem consists of the midbrain, the pons, and the medulla. The midbrain is not well developed in man. The pons serves as the primary base for supporting the cerebellar hemispheres. The medulla is directly continuous with the spinal cord. The brain stem contains many important nervous centers and gives rise to all twelve pairs of cranial nerves. The cerebellar hemispheres are concerned with the involuntary coordination and regulation of skeletal activity, particularly in postural movements. The cerebral hemispheres reaches their highest level of development in man. The cerebral cortex contains the centers for all higher mental activities. The advanced specialization and development of the cerebral hemispheres is largely responsible for the superiority of the human brain over that of lower animals.

The *spinal cord* has been subdivided into cervical, thoracic, lumbar, sacral, and coccygeal levels. It is segmented throughout, each segment giving rise to a pair of spinal nerves that are distributed to corresponding levels of the trunk and extremities. Usually there are 31 pairs of spinal nerves: 8 cervical, 12 thoracic, 5 lumbar, 5 sacral, and 1 coccygeal. The spinal cord is the primary site for most reflex activity of the trunk and extremities and contains the many important nervous pathways that ascend to and descend from the brain.

When the brain or spinal cord is sectioned (Fig. 5-1) two types of nervous tissue are grossly apparent: gray matter, consisting largely of nerve cell bodies, and white matter, consisting chiefly of nerve fibers and pathways and outgrowths, or processes, of the nerve cells. The nerve cell

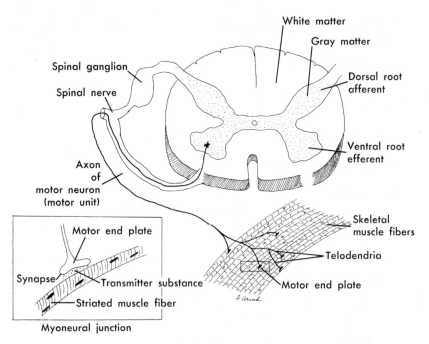

Fig. 5-1. Cross-section of spinal cord and associated motor unit and enlargement of myoneural junction.

bodies of the gray matter are the primary loci for nervous function. The nerve fibers that comprise the white matter, on the other hand, serve as pathways connecting various levels of the nervous system.

The CNS is well protected from injury by the meningeal layers that invest it and by the bony skull and vertebrae that encase the brain and spinal cord. The cranial nerves emerge from the brain stem through foramina in the skull, and the spinal nerves emerge through foramina between successive vertebrae.

Peripheral nervous system

The cranial nerves, the spinal nerves, and the peripheral parts of the autonomic nervous system, which together comprise the peripheral nervous system, serve as the lines of communication between the CNS and the skin, muscle, and viscera of the body. A nerve is a bundle of thousands of nerve fibers, of which there are several types differing in such characteristics as diameter, rate of conduction, and connections within the CNS. Nerve fibers differ in their functional capacities and therefore are referred to as the functional components of nerves.

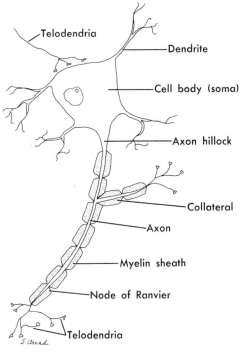

Telodendria

Dendrite

Cell body (soma)

Axon hillock

Collateral

Axon

Myelin sheath

Node of Ranvier

Telodendria

Fig. 5-2. Motoneuron.

FUNCTIONAL COMPONENTS OF THE NERVOUS SYSTEM

The nervous system has two functional components: *afferent*, or sensory, component and the *efferent*, or motor, component. The afferent component consists of sensory neurons, and the efferent component consists of motoneurons. The neuron is the basic structural unit of the nervous system and is composed of cell body, axon, dendrite, and neuronal covering. The nerve impulse is transmitted along the neural structure. If the impulse is of peripheral sensory origin it is afferent and travels toward the CNS; if the impulse is of central origin it is efferent and travels to the effector mechanism. Neurons can be classified not only according to their function but also according to their structure, or type of neural covering. For our purposes we will be concerned only with the functional classification.

The *neuron* is a nerve cell and consists of three primary parts (Fig. 5-2). There is a *cell body*, or *soma*, a multibranched portion composed of *dendrites*, and a usually long portion called the *axon*. The soma and the dendrites are the sites of neural impulse transmission; that is, neural impulses are transmitted from one neuron to another at the dendrite and the soma. Axons, being the terminal end of the neuron, impinge upon the dendrites or soma of the next neuron. The terminal ends of the neurons are called telodendria and function as chemical (or electrical) transmitters carrying the nerve impulse from the axon to the dendrite or soma of the next cell. The microscopic space between the telodendria of one neuron and the dendrite and soma of the next is called a *synaptic* cleft. The soma also plays a part in the growth and nutrition of the neuron. Functionally, then, the axon is a long projection of the neuron that carries nerve impulses away from the cell body, toward the periphery; the dendrite is a more diffuse projection of the neuron that carries action potentials toward the soma.

Afferent, or sensory, neurons conduct nerve impulses from the sensory receptors to the CNS. The cell body of an afferent neuron is located outside the spinal column in the dorsal root ganglion. The dendrite and axon of an afferent neuron are usually longer than those of an efferent neuron. There are three functional types of afferent neurons: *somatic afferent neurons,* sensory neurons from receptors in the skin, skeletal muscles, joints, and tendons; *visceral afferent neurons,* sensory neurons from receptors in the internal organs and blood vessels; and *special afferent neurons,* sensory neurons from receptor organs of special sense, such as eyes, ears, and olfactory processes.

Efferent neurons, or motoneurons, conduct nerve impulses to the response mechanisms of the organism, such as the muscles and the glands. The cell body of a motoneuron is usually located closer to the dendrites than that of an afferent neuron. There are two functional types of efferent neurons: *somatic efferent neurons,* motoneurons from the CNS to the skeletal muscle; and *visceral efferent neurons,* motoneurons from the CNS to smooth muscle of blood vessels and internal organs, to cardiac muscle, and to the glands.

The motoneuron, the aspect of the motor system that most concerns us here, is aptly described as the "final common pathway" of the effector system (Sherrington, 1961).[1] All central nervous control over the muscles, whether excitatory or inhibitory, is effected by the motoneuron. We must keep in mind, however, that except in the experimental neurophysiologic situation, a change in the activity of the motoneuron automatically effects changes in the activity of the afferent system that in turn have a profound effect upon the motoneuron; that is, the aspect of the afferent system that signals muscle length and tension in turn affects the action of the muscle in question. The motoneuron can be viewed as a controller element in a self-regulating system. This self-regulating system might be considered the functional element upon which higher (CNS) and other influences must be played. It should be kept in mind that the primary sources of sensory input providing feedback to the moving system, the muscle spindles are themselves subject to influence by the CNS, and the tension feedback loop, the Golgi tendon organs, is also subject to modulation within lower structures—the interneuron relay.

MOTOR UNIT AND SKELETAL MUSCLE

Muscle is the effector or response agent for CNS activity. Muscle is the organ of overt behavioral response in man. Muscle contracts and in so doing performs work. Muscle activity is limited to contraction and relaxation. The contraction of skeletal muscle is the means by which the organism reacts to its external environment. All striated muscles of the body cross one or more skeletal articulations and are thus responsible for angular displacement of the two bones comprising the given articulation.

The *motor unit* is the functional unit of the effector system. The motor unit consists of a single motoneuron with multiple terminals and all its associated muscle fibers. It is the smallest unit of muscular activity. It must be emphasized that the twitch of a single motor unit is quite different from the smooth, graded, and coordinated behavioral response occurring during normal movement. The movement of a limb to pick up a cup, for example, involves participation of many motor units, depending upon the direction and extent of the action and force involved. Fig. 5-1 shows the motor unit with its cell body located in the horn and the associated nerve fiber passing out the ventral root and traveling to the individual muscle. As the nerve fiber of each motor unit reaches the muscle, it divides, each small nerve fiber articulating with a single muscle fiber. This dividing of the motor unit nerve fiber determines the *innervation ratio*. The innervation ratio is an indication of the size of a particular motor unit. The innervation ratio depends on the function of the muscle and can range from 3:1 for small muscles concerned with fine muscular control, such as those in the hand, to 150:1 for large muscles, such as those in the leg and trunk.

Activation of a single motor unit is the weakest possible muscular contraction. As force or precision of movement is required, more motor units are activated and involved. Three things occur in overlapping sequence to produce force: (1) recruitment of additional motor units, (2) a more active graded motor unit discharge, and (3) the summation of the graded motor unit involvement. The total tension developing at any instant in time is the sum of all the tensions being developed by each motor unit at that moment. Motor unit activity is thus graded and asynchronous in the involvement in coordinated movement.

Much recent work has been done with conditioning of single motor units (Basmajian, 1967, 1973; Hefferline, Bruno and Davidowitz, 1971). This work has essentially demonstrated that humans can learn selectively and voluntarily to control single motor units. Experiments of this type have been useful for two reasons. They have helped elucidate the underlying control processes and the effects of conscious versus unconscious regulation of motor activity, and they have aided the clinician in areas such as biofeedback techniques for tension reduction and regulation. Using electromyographic feedback techniques, subjects can learn to activate instantly and upon command a single motor unit. They can keep the motor unit active for long periods of time and can even learn to produce rhythmic patterns with single motor units. The fact that human subjects can control single and groups of motor units is especially significant in the study of the control processes underlying human movement. Through a complex array of procedures, subjects learn to shift activity from one group of motor units to another in controlling their movement. This capability obviously provides the mover with an extremely complex, variable, and flexible system for movement.

Fig. 5-1 schematically depicts a single motor unit and an enlarged view of the myoneural junction. Structurally, the motor unit is composed of the motoneuron (axon, dendrite, and soma) and the multiple terminals that divide prior to their termination at the myoneural junction (neuromotor synapse).

The events leading to the contraction of the muscle fibers associated with a motor unit are as follows: (1) An impulse is conducted along the efferent motoneuron to its termination at the myoneural junction. (2) The neural impulse causes a depolarization of the nerve terminal, resulting in the liberation of a chemical transmitter substance called *acetylcholine* (ACh), which is stored in the neuronal terminals of axons. The ACh diffuses across the small gap (synapse) between the nerve ending and the motor end-plate. This is a process of chemical transmission, activated by an electrical depolarization at the axonal terminal. (3) The chemical substances ACh produces an excitation on the muscle cell membrane and motor end-plate, and the excitation in turn produces a wave of depolarization within the individual muscle fiber. The depolarization produces what we call a muscle twitch or contraction. The twitch is an all-or-none phenomenon; the individual muscle fiber either contracts completely or not at all. A certain amount of transmitter substance—the threshold level for the muscle end-plate—must be liberated before the wave of depolarization will occur.

The events that occur between the arrival of the impulse at the nerve ending or motor end-plate and the initiation of the impulse in the muscle fiber are collectively called *neuromuscular transmission*. The events that occur between muscle fiber depolarization and actual contraction of the muscle are referred to as *excitation-conduction coupling*. The activation of the motor unit produces a summation of the tensions of all its associated muscle fibers.

Types of muscle

There are three types of muscle: cardiac, smooth, and skeletal. Cardiac and smooth muscle are similar in structure and lack the characteristic bands or striations of skeletal muscle. Our study is concerned with skeletal muscle, sometimes referred to as striated or extrafusal muscle. Skeletal muscle is unlike either cardiac or smooth muscle in that contraction is brought about by a stimulus from the motoneuron—the nerve impulse and neuromuscular transmission just described. If the motor nerve innervating the muscle fiber is not intact, the muscle fiber is unable voluntarily to contract.

Skeletal muscle is made up of many muscle fibers. This multiple arrangement of muscle fibers is bound together by connective tissue that fuses at each end of the muscle to form a fascia, or tendon, that in turn is attached across an articulation to the successive limb segment. The tendon attaches the muscle to a bone. (Muscle structure-function relationships will be discussed in Chapter Eight.)

RECEPTORS

Receptors are specialized nerve endings adapted and sensitive to different kinds of stimuli or energy. The term receptor is used mostly in relation to organs of special sense (retina, cochlea) or structures associated with terminals of peripheral afferent nerves (muscle spindles, Golgi tendon organs, joint receptors, etc.) Without these specialized receptive structures, we would have no means by which to obtain information about the environment or our internal state or about the ongoing activity resulting from our movements. The receptor is a *transducer* that changes (transduces) one form of energy (stretch, tension, pressure, light, heat) into another form of energy—such as electrical—in the neural impulse. The function of a receptor is, therefore, to detect a stimulus and to respond in such a way as ultimately to increase or decrease the rate of discharge of propagated impulses in the nerves associated with the receptive field. The energy released is the result of metabolic activity previously stored in the responding structure. Three categories of receptors can be identified according to location of receptor:

1. *Exteroceptors,* or *teloreceptors*—receptors used to pick up and classify information coming from the external environment, usually a distance from the body. Receptors such as eyes, ears, and nose are classified as exteroceptors.
2. *Interoreceptors*—receptors located in the viscera, and receptors responsible for sense of pain, touch, pressure, and temperature.
3. *Proprioceptors*—receptors responsible for sense of position of the body and limbs; these include muscles, tendons, joints, and vestibular mechanism.

Of primary concern are the receptors that provide information about the actual movement itself—*movement-produced stimulation*—and the moment-to-moment position of the limbs and body. With respect to goal-directed human movement, the eyes, and to a lesser extent the ears, provide the performer with information about events external to the organism. *Movement-produced stimulation* provides the system with information about active movements (Konorski, 1967). This is one form of sensory feedback that provides the CNS with information about the results and moment-to-moment progress of our actions.

We can no longer view the skeletal links, the limb segments, as being under the passive control of the CNS, or, as Bernstein (1967) states, as being "unequivocally subservient to these impulses." In effect, what we now find is that a given nerve impulse may produce entirely different effects given the variation in external forces and internal conditions. The CNS, through afferent information feedback, must adapt to both internal and external forces. The essential point is that sensory feedback— information received from receptors—provides information to the CNS against which adjustments in the muscular actions are made. Sensory feedback has two important functions in a self-regulatory system involving the control of posture and movement: (1) compensation of disturbances causing disruption of intended output, and (2) following changes within the regulatory system itself.

There are three types of sensory information resulting from movement-produced stimulation: kinesthetic, somesthetic/proprioceptive, and visual (Higgins, 1972). This distinction is useful not only in a control context but also in discussing specific sensory receptors and their functions. The terms proprioception and kinesthesis have been used interchangably for many years. On a behavioral level they have come to mean perception of movement and posture of the body and limbs in time and space. From a sensory receptor point of view we shall make a clearer distinction. *Kinesthetic* sensory information is information derived from the stretch receptors located in the muscle fibers and from Golgi tendon organs located in the tendonous attachments of muscles, which together provide the CNS with information about active movement produced by the CNS itself. *Somesthetic/proprioceptive* sensory information is information derived from receptors located in the joints and skin, which together provide the CNS with information about limb and body posture and touch and pressure. *Visual* sensory information is derived through exteroceptors and provides information related to the spatial and temporal relationships existing between the body, limbs, and the environment.

Kinesthetic sensory information is the result of movement-produced stimulation only, whereas somesthetic/proprioceptive and visual sensory information can be the result of movement-produced stimulation or external force or both. (Higgins, 1972:315.)

We will now discuss each sensory system and the respective receptors responsible for providing information to the control system. Following the discussion of the systems, a brief overview of the total control system involved in the self-regulating system will be presented.

Kinesthetic sensory system

As distinguished from the somesthetic/proprioceptive system, the kinesthetic sensory system is concerned with evaluating muscular length, rate of change of muscular length, and muscular tension. These evaluations are made independent of displacement information derived from the joints, which are part of the somesthetic/proprioceptive sensory system. The sensory receptors responsible for providing this information are the muscle spindle receptors, located in the intrafusal muscle fibers, and the Golgi tendon organs, located in the tendons (Eccles, 1973; Granit, 1970; Konorski, 1967).

The *muscle spindle* is one of the two principal muscle sensory receptors. It is a "differential-length receptor," distributed throughout and associated in parallel with extrafusal (contractile) muscle (Granit, 1970; Stark, 1968). It is of importance in human motor coordination due to two primary functions: its positional feedback characteristics influence the stretch reflex in postural control, and its kinesthetic feedback properties provide information useful in CNS control of complex coordinated movement. Functionally, the muscle spindle operates within a system that has both motor (efferent) and sensory (afferent) properties; that is, it has both contractile and sensory properties. The muscle spindle consists of four to six intrafusal muscle fibers grouped in bundles with two types of receptor organs (Fig. 5-3). *Intrafusal muscle fibers* are a class of muscle and, although they have contractile properties, they contract only very weakly and thus do not contribute to the overall force exerted by a contracting muscle. Their function is to govern "the frequency of the discharge of impulses from the length detectors," that is, the afferent nerves coming from the spindle itself (Granit, 1970:1). *Extrafusal muscle fibers* compose the skeletal muscles of the body. Their contractile properties provide the required force for maintenance of posture and regulation of movement.

Muscle spindles are connected in parallel with and proximally to the extrafusal fibers. Distally they are connected to either the tendon or the endomysium (connective tissue surrounding the muscle fiber) of the extrafusal fibers (Granit, 1955). The ends, or *polar regions*, of the spindle are the contractile element, and the central, or *equatorial region*, is the

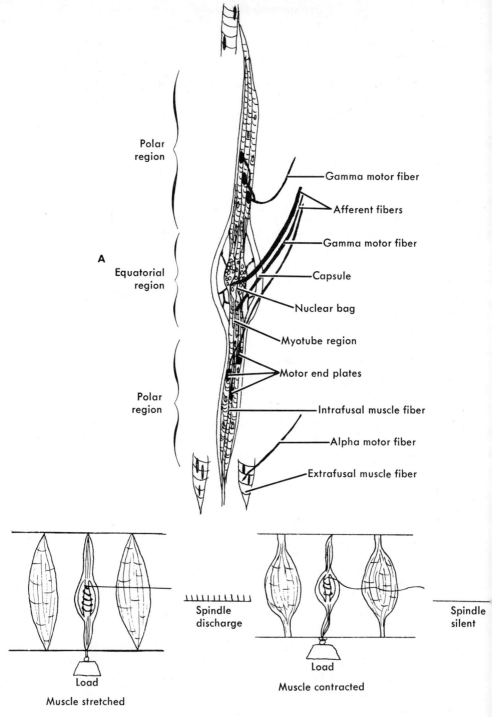

Polar region

Equatorial region

Polar region

A

Gamma motor fiber

Afferent fibers

Gamma motor fiber

Capsule

Nuclear bag

Myotube region

Motor end plates

Intrafusal muscle fiber

Alpha motor fiber

Extrafusal muscle fiber

Spindle discharge

Spindle silent

Load

Load

Muscle stretched

Muscle contracted

B

Fig. 5-3. Muscle spindle. (**A** adapted from Barker, 1948; **B** adapted from Ruch, Patton, Woodbury, and Towe, 1966.)

sensory element of the spindle. The polar region contains the intrafusal muscle fibers, which are long and slender. The equatorial region is unstriated and noncontractile and is made up of a nuclear-bag region and a myotube region, both giving rise to afferent innervation. The polar regions give rise to efferent innervation (called the gamma motor system). Thus muscle spindles are innervated by both afferent and efferent nerves. For a more detailed discussion of each of these innervations and their functional significance, the reader is referred to Mountcastle (1974) and Thompson (1967), and for the most detailed treatment to Granit (1970).

The functional significance of the muscle spindle in the control of movement lies in its ability to serve the self-regulating system. The muscle spindles both provide and receive information from the CNS, thereby insuring the modification and control of the extrafusal fibers and the spindles themselves. *Afferent fibers arising from the muscle spindle relay information concerning length and rate of change of length of the extrafusal muscle to the spinal cord.* This information in turn affects the efferent fibers (both the alpha and gamma motor nerves) supplying the extrafusal fibers and the intrafusal fibers of the muscle spindle. This feedback and influence effects the afferent discharge coming from the muscle spindle. The gamma motor fibers influence the muscle spindle by contracting the intrafusal fibers and thereby taking up the slack in the spindle and causing a change in rate of firing of the spindle through the afferent system. This "fusimotor" activity provides "a mechanism for maintaining a sensory message from the spindles proportional to the amount of external stretch even under changing conditions of muscle contraction" (Patton, 1966:203). Muscle spindles are thus controlled not only by the degree of muscle stretch but also by the action of efferent fibers referred to as gamma motor fibers.

Functionally, then, the muscle spindle determines the difference in length of extrafusal and intrafusal fibers (Henneman, 1974). When the extrafusal fibers are stretched, the intrafusal fibers, being in parallel with the extrafusal fibers, are also stretched. Stretching the intrafusal fiber produces an afferent discharge from the spindle that reflexly causes a shortening (contraction) of the extrafusal fiber. Alpha motor fibers affect the shortening of the extrafusal fibers. It has been shown that the gamma motor system stimulates the intrafusal fibers in parallel with the alpha motor neuron stimulation of the extrafusal fibers. The gamma motor input to the spindles thus causes shortening of intrafusal fibers that takes up the slack in the intrafusal fiber. The muscle spindle is rendered capable of altering its afferent discharge, which then may lead to extrafusal fiber shortening. The integration of spindle information results from a comparison of the spindle output with the intended action (or preset spindle), which very likely occurs in cerebellum. In this situation the muscle spindle is seen to signal the length of the muscle as a whole (Granit, 1970; Henneman, 1974; Stark, 1968).

The gamma motor system has three primary functions in the control of movement: the maintenance of spindle length in direct correspondence to the length of the muscle, the control of reflex muscular activity necessary for postural control, and the presetting or biasing of the muscle spindle for a predetermined level of sensory function in voluntary movement.

Muscle spindle information and the monosynaptic reflex connections together provide one of the most basic yet complex elements in the motor control system. The spindles minimize changes in muscle length resulting from external disturbing forces such as gravity and in addition provide the CNS with a simple means for carrying out the changes in length (Henneman, 1974).

In contrast to the muscle spindle, the *Golgi tendon organ* (GTO) responds to increases in muscular tension rather than to changes in length. GTOs consist of specialized tissue encapsulated within the tendon and are located at the junctions of the muscle fibers and their respective tendons. A sensory neuron transmits the sensory impulse from the receptor to the cord. GTOs are functionally and structurally arranged in series with the muscle again in contrast with the muscle spindle, which is arranged in parallel with the muscle. Being in series with the muscle, the GTO responds to stretch, whether brought about by active contraction of the muscle or by some form of passive stretch. Research indicates that the GTO responds more to stretch brought about by muscular tension, that is, active contraction of the muscle. The GTOs transduce active or passive tension and have been found to be sensitive to the rate of increase in tension (Granit, 1970; Henneman, 1974).

> The relative insensitivity of these endings to ordinary degrees of passive stretch gave rise to the belief that they functioned primarily to protect muscle from damage by signaling when excessive stretch occurred. Actually the tendon organ is an extremely sensitive receptor if the stimulus is appropriate. . . . Apparently a tendon organ samples the local tensions in a muscle by monitoring a minute fraction of the muscle fibers of a number of motor units. The response of a tendon organ is determined by the number of active motor units inserting on it and the tension developed by each of the contributing fibers. (Henneman, 1974:634.)

The afferent signals arising from the GTOs are transmitted to the spinal cord, where they elicit both an inhibitory and a facilitory effect on the motoneurons, an inhibitory effect on the agonist muscle and a facilatory effect on the antagonist. Therefore, information feedback about tension is thought to help compensate for the variations in movement and probably aids in the compensation of variation resulting from length and velocity.

Proprioceptive/somesthetic system

The proprioceptive/somesthetic system is responsible for providing and evaluating the sensory information derived from receptors located in the joints and the skin. The psychophysical literature is replete with data suggesting that the human organism can accurately detect joint displacement (movement at a single joint) and steady state of joint position (extent of movement). It is therefore the functional role of the receptors located in and about the joints to provide information about rate of movement, direction of movement, and extent of movement. In a sense, these sensory receptors measure the displacement produced by the contraction of the skeletal muscles but say nothing about the muscles themselves. They convey no information about length, rate of change of length, and tension.

The angular displacement, position, and resistance to movement is determined by nerve endings located around the joint capsule (Ruffini type endings) and a few receptors (similar to Pacinian corpules) found in pericapsular tissue located on the articular surfaces (Mountcastle, 1974). On the basis of the type of afferent nerve innervation and receptor type, three basic kinds of sensory information are transmitted: occurrence of a mechanical event, absolute detection of movement, and absolute detection of position (Mountcastle, 1974).

Receptors located in the skin may also play a role in motor control, but the exact function is not clear, and without a lengthy discussion about levels of afferent innervation and cortical connections, little if any application to our problems can be made.

Visual sensory system

The visual sensory system provides information about the spatial and temporal events and relationships occurring in the environment. This can mean simply information about the location and movement of objects in the environment, the rate at which objects are moving, and the spatial and temporal relationship between objects in the environment. In addition, important visual information is provided about the location of our limbs and body in relation to the environment and in relation to themselves.

Vision is the reception by the eye of light from light sources and reflecting surfaces in the environment. It is brought about by stimulation of the retina, which contains the sensory receptors of the eye. The pattern of retinal stimulation is dependent upon the position of the eye, head, and body in relation to the light. The visual system is one of the major information-gathering systems of the body. A more detailed discussion of the function and structure of the eye and the processes of vision is beyond the scope of this book. For a most lucid and readable treatment of vision, the reader is referred to Gregory (1966).

Labyrinth

The membranous labyrinth (inner ear) is the main sensory element concerned with orientation of the head with respect to gravity and equilibrium during active movement. The function of the labyrinths is to detect acceleration. Linear acceleration is detected by two sacklike structures, the saccule and the utricle. Angular acceleration (rotation of the head) is sensed by three semicircular canals arranged in planes at right angles to one another, thereby providing for full analysis as to plane of rotational acceleration. Each labyrinth thus contains the means to provide information on orientation of the head in space when stationary and angular and linear acceleration of the head, during motion. Because of their constant activity the labyrinths provide a steady input to the CNS and thus allow constant evaluation of acceleration and deceleration characteristics of the head. Though this system is only indirectly concerned with voluntary movement, along with the portions of the cerebellum it constitutes a powerful system for the mediation of static and dynamic posture. The labyrinths work as a synergistic pair with respect to angular accelerations. For example, when a canal on the right is stimulated by acceleration, its counterpart on the left produces a decreased output of activity.

In the human it is thought that the eyes and cervical articulations play a large role in orienting and maintaining equilibrium (Bizzi, 1974; Easton, 1972). It is no doubt safe to assume that the combined inputs from the labyrinths, eyes, and cervical articulations assume a major functional role in providing information to the CNS regarding ongoing positional and movement cues of the body and the head.

REFLEXES AND PURPOSEFUL HUMAN MOVEMENT

Reflexes are an integral part of the moving human system. Simply stated, a *reflex* is usually an involuntary, invariable, adaptive response to a stimulus. It is a local and stereotyped response involving specific segments, muscles, and usually a particular level of the spinal cord. The reflex probably represents the most fundamental level of nervous system functional movement control. The same muscles used in volitional activity are observed in reflex activity; the resultant reflexive movements are stereotypic and respond in very specific ways to specific stimuli. Reflexes are thought to be basic responses that occur even when higher centers of the brain are removed or destroyed. Normally, reflexes are not entirely independent of higher brain centers but rather can be influenced and even dominated by them. This is especially true of reflexes involving skeletal muscle. The reflex may play an important role in early development of patterns of movement (Bruner, 1971). The early crawling pattern of the infant may be established by the asymmetric tonic neck reflex (ATNR) resulting from the infant's turning of the head. For example, when the head is turned to the right, corresponding extension of the right shoulder and elbow joint and left hip and knee joint occurs with flexion of the left shoulder and elbow joint and right hip and knee joint. The fact that these movements, opposing flexion and extension, occur reflexively produces sensory input from the moving limbs. This movement-produced stimulation provides feedback that the infant could theoretically use in the continued development of a motor program ultimately resulting in volitional crawling.

It is possible that these reflexes continue to function as components of volitional activity even though the movements for completing a task are extremely complex. The reflex utilizes the same muscles as does the volitional movement (Easton, 1972). They are a part of the total movement and represent fragments of the coordinated movement (Easton, 1972). Some reflexes, especially the tonic neck reflex, tend to bias the subsequent movement in the direction of gaze, a response needed for obtaining environmental information. With the turning of the head toward a sound, for example, the performer extends the arm to that side as though a preparatory motion was set up prior to final execution. Several writers interested in motor control problems have noted that the reflex may serve as a tuning device that establishes a baseline of muscular activity and movement against which the subsequent aspects of the movement can be performed. The reader may wish to think about how many sport activities involve movements (rotation) of the head with corresponding flexion and extension of contralateral limbs—for example, in archery or the basketball jumpshot. As Easton (1972:591) has stated, the reflexes may serve as "the raw material from which the central nervous system may build volitional movements." The reflexes may serve as the prefabricated building blocks for volitional movement. The more complex control is directed against a known background of neuromuscular activity brought about by the reflex. The contracting muscles and moving segments provide an important source of movement-produced information at the outset of a given action. This allows the higher centers to program the subsequent ongoing activity and produce the finely coordinated, successful movement.

CENTRAL CONTROL

How does a system that transforms, integrates and stores information and effects change control human movement? How are reflexes, environmental information, moment-to-moment state of the organism's movement or limb and body position, and the performer's intention for action integrated to produce a goal-directed movement?

The control and regulation of movement is ultimately the responsibility of the nervous system. The necessary precursor for the control of our voluntary movements is information about environmental conditions, the state of our body, muscles, tendons, and joints, and some idea about how to move (the intention of the action). Our movements are reflections of how the system resolves the various sources of variation described in Chapter Three. Sommerhoff (1974) identifies two important facts concerning CNS organization and movement: movements are the end product of the integration of a variety of levels within the brain and spinal cord, and the full learning capabilities for movement reside in the cerebral cortex and possibly the cerebellum and spinal cord as well.

These neural systems are no doubt organized as a result of our social history, the way tools are used to transform our environment, and the development of receptive and expressive language (Luria, 1968). The complex neural systems function as mediators between experience (our social history) and the environment (use of tools, object identification, etc.). The primary function of the nervous system, therefore, is to mediate between these internal and external states.

The CNS is a complex anatomic structure made up of innumerable neural aggregates and fiber tracts, and its primary function is one of mediating between external and internal states and events. Our understanding of motor control processes involved in voluntary movement and related neurologic correlates has moved from the classical position of narrow localization of neural structures and direct functional relationships to a much more integrative position that perceives an integration of neural aggregates that will ensure the function of complex systems within systems.

Until the early 1960s control and execution of movement were thought of as a direct input-output mechanism or function—a passive system. This notion grew out of stimulus-response psychology and the reflex arc of neurophysiology. "The ubiquitous presence of feedback and feedforward mechanisms (e.g., CNS control of receptor function) necessitates a modification of this view" (Pribram, 1972:96). The CNS is now conceptualized as involving a complex set of hierarchically organized operations or sets of aggregates of expectations (Sommerhoff, 1974). It is an active not a passive, system, which means that the organism is actively seeking information and constantly acting upon this information. "Thus the fundamental data the brain must process are not passively received sensory stimuli, but rather, actively achieved input transformation" (Sommerhoff, 1974). It is the role of the CNS to control not only its output but also its input.

One way to proceed is to delineate four basic CNS mechanisms involved in motor control: (1) brain stem, reticular formation, and medial and basal cortex, or midbrain; (2) cerebellum; (3) cerebral cortex—two hemispheres, each made up of temporal, occipital, parietal, and frontal lobes; and (4) sensory and motor pathways.

The output of the CNS is the result of a multilevel process of integration. Its total effect is a kind of modulation or sculpturing of input and reactions from all levels, which ultimately can result in

> precise matching of action to environment. This sculpturing may be effected either by selective excitation or selective inhibition. In this manner the higher centers achieve the required level of discrimination in the evaluation of the stimulus situation and of articulation in the execution of the motor responses. (Sommerhoff, 1974:153.)

Midbrain

The primary function of the midbrain structures is to maintain the neural tone needed for the working function of the cerebral cortex. Disruption of this area causes, among other things, impairment of vigilance and emotion but does not directly affect perception or movement.

Cerebellum

The cerebellum receives an abundance of information from all afferent sources. A predominant input is from the muscle receptors—muscle spindles and GTOs. The cerebellum appears to play no role in conscious sensation; it does not mediate sensation. Structural and functional evidence, however, does indicate clearly that the cerebellum is intimately involved in the elaboration of motor activity. Recent work has even suggested that much "motor learning" occurs at this neural level (Evarts and Thach, 1971; Ito, 1970). This structure is closely linked with the labyrinthian system and is concerned with maintenance of balance. It functions to maintain muscular tone necessary for posture both at rest and in motion. It also plays a major role in coordination of movement and the perfection and precision of motor skill (Sommerhoff, 1974). At a structural level the cerebellum can establish closed loops with the motoneurons through the rubrospinal, reticulospinal, and the vestibulospinal systems. The rubrospinal system mediates flexion. The reticulospinal system probably mediates postural effects relative to actions on the right and left sides of the body. The vestibulospinal system, on the other hand, may mediate fast responses to the muscle spindle input.

The significance of the cerebellum is related primarily to the regulation and production of coordinated movement and to the influence on cortical activity. Current thinking suggests that the output from the cerebellum to the cortex reflects the input from the cerebellum's abundant afferent sources, including the muscle receptors.

Cerebral cortex

The higher centers of nervous function are contained in the two hemispheres that are folded and convoluted over both the midbrain and the cerebellum. Each hemisphere can be divided anatomically into four lobes. The *temporal lobe* receives auditory input and deals with complicated forms of acoustic analysis. The *occipital lobe* receives primarily visual information and is capable of coding, decoding, and storing the information. The *parietal lobe* receives information related to proprioception, touch, body position, and external-world orientation. Lesions in any of these regions affect normal inflow of information and profoundly disturb the normal coding and retrieval of information. The *frontal lobe* of the cortex is divided into premotor, supplementary, and frontal areas. The premotor area is most closely involved in voluntary movements and is topographically organized. Movements that appear to be automatic are though to be the result of the supplemental motor area's influence upon the premotor area. The frontal region receives information from the posterior association areas and the temporal lobes, where further elaboration and integration occurs. As a whole the frontal motor cortex is thought to be responsible for programming of movements and actions, for the regulation of active processes that are being performed, and perhaps for matching the effect of actions with original intention of acts. Lesions in this region produce serious disturbances of movements, actions, and organization of actions in accordance with what is desired.

Sensory and motor pathways

There are no point-to-point afferent (sensory) pathways for representation in the cortex. Even though one pathway may be modality specific and topographically organized and another may be slow, diffuse and multirelayed, neither is point to point. Most pathways have projections to various levels and are in turn influenced by descending cortical pathways. "No region of the cortex acts like a television screen on which a true picture of the outer world unfolds" (Sommerhoff, 1974:153). The efferent (motor) pathways are contained in the pyramidal system and travel from the cortex to the motor neuron pool of the cord. One-third of the system's fibers originate in the motor cortex (pyramidal tract) and are responsible for less stereotypic and more finely adapted movement components. The extrapyramidal system is responsible for the gross features of movement as well as the more automatic movements involved in balance.

The motoneurons receive input from spindles and GTOs, which are believed also to send collaterals to the higher supraspinal centers. Constituting a system of closed loops, this afferent activity is thought to affect the activity at various neurologic levels of the descending efferent pathways. This is accomplished either through direct neural connection, or more likely through "interneurons" by influencing or impinging upon both alpha and gamma motoneurons.

It has been demonstrated that the cerebral cortex may receive some input from the muscle afferents (spindle and GTOs) (Granit, 1970). This movement-produced stimulation may be used for formulation and reformulation of motor plans. There is little evidence that the cortex uses this spindle and GTO information in the elaboration of its output to the muscles; hence, the notion of conscious muscle sense should be dispelled. The cortex does receive information related to the position of the articular surfaces (joint position sense). It appears that these inputs have little influence at the spinal cord level. We can with some justification say, therefore, that the cerebral cortex operates in terms of position and changes in position; that is, movements are the result of a high degree of functional organization, much of which is built into the cord and the brain stem. For example, the phase leading properties of the gamma motor system can preset the level of spindle activity prior to the initiation of a movement; hence, the final control for that movement rests with the integration of afferent and efferent information at the cord level. It is actions and not muscles or movements that are programmed by the cortex. This notion leads us to the realization that the many aspects of a movement, the final control of the musculature, is left to more peripheral, infraspinal processes.

SUMMARY

New insights and findings continue to be put forth that either add support to what we already know or alter long-held positions and interpretations of how the neurologic system functions in the regulation and control of our movements.

What should be clear by now is that the central organization of movement is highly dependent upon mechanisms capable of translating afferent sensory input into efferent response processes. Given the inextricable link between the motor and the sensory systems, we can say that

> the organization of action is to a large extent the management of receptors embedded in the contractile tissue of muscle (muscle spindles) or in the tendons that attach muscles to bones and joints. These receptors react not only to the contractions of muscle, whether produced by external forces or by nerve impulses originating in the brain (via a system of efferent fibers labeled alpha because of their large diameter) but also to excitations reaching them directly via the gamma efferent fiber system. The immediate organization of movement is therefore

dependent on a process that involves receptors, afferents from those receptors to the spinal cord, efferents from there to contractile muscles, *and to receptors*. (Pribram, 1971:221.)

NOTES

1. The term "final common pathway," first used by Sherrington (1961), emphasizes the fact that all influence over skeletal muscles exerted by the CNS must be channeled through these neurons, the integrated output of which, in the form of trains of all-or-nothing nerve impulses, initiates all normal contraction of skeletal muscles.

SIX

Environmental constraints and their significance in the organization of movement

The performance environment is the spatial and temporal configuration of elements in the world external to the performer. This environment places certain demands on the organization of our movements. For effective goal accomplishment, the spatial and temporal elements in the environment must be *matched* by our movements. Matching movements to the environmental constraints also involves interaction with constraints imposed by biomechanical and morphologic factors. Coordinated, effective, goal-directed movements are possible only because of the predictable features of environmental, biomechanical, and morphologic factors. Environmental constraints, therefore, relate to the predictability of the spatial and temporal elements in the environment and the absence or presence of spatial and temporal changes between trials (intertrial variability). Biomechanical and morphologic constraints as features of goal-directed movements are discussed in Chapters Seven and Eight.

All human movement is organized in terms of space and time. This chapter considers the spatial and temporal components of movements themselves, the basic assumption being that goal-directed movements are spatially and temporally regulated and coordinated. This regulation requires that attention be given to the constraints imposed by the environment since the environment has such a profound effect upon the spatial and temporal organization of our movements (Gentile et al., 1975).

SPATIAL AND TEMPORAL ELEMENTS OF THE ENVIRONMENT

By nature an implicit feature of the environment is continuous space and time. The concepts of space and time are viewed as continua—space an infinite three-dimensional continuum and time an infinite one-dimensional continuum (Feather, 1970). Space can be described as a system of related and defined objects occurring within a boundless three-dimensional extent. Time can be described as a system of past and present sequential relations that any event or object has with another. Space and time always occur together. However, for convenience and, more importantly, for determining the relationship between environment and organization of movement, the spatial and temporal elements are described separately.

The spatial elements of the environment pertain to the relative position of objects in space. The temporal elements of the environment pertain to the sequential relationship between events and objects in space. For example, when a performer addresses a golf ball prior to initiating the swing there is a specific arrangement of elements in the environment, the position of the ball being the primary element. There are no temporal elements affecting the ball and thus it can be said that the environment is spatially and temporally stable. At the other end of the continuum, the batter preparing to hit a pitched baseball has to contend with changing spatial and temporal elements and variability from trial to trial (intertrial variability). Spatially the baseball occupies a new position for each sequential point in time. The spatial and temporal elements of the environment vary together—they are, so to speak, interacting—so we say that the environment is unstable.

An additional factor that the teacher and researcher in motor skills must contend with is the absence or presence of intertrial variability. Using golf again as the example, each shot is made with the ball in a new and usually unique spatial location. The movement will therefore be organized in relation to this new spatial location even though there is certainty and hence a high degree of predictability with reference to spatial and temporal parameters of the ball for each shot. In other words, the location of the ball changes from shot to shot, but for any given swing of the club the ball will not change position in space or time. The resultant movement is therefore organized on the basis of the location of the ball on the field of play and upon the performer's selection of the appropriate club. (With reference to this last point, the reader should remember that each club because of its unique weight and design characteristics also influences the way in which the movement is organized. Each club has a unique feel and accomplishes a specific end in relation to the performance outcome. Aspects such as weight, size, and feel of the implement used by the performer are classified as biomechanical constraints. Mention is made here in order to help the reader understand the overall conceptual basis of environmental constraints.)

In many skills classified as closed skills the performance environment is stable and predictable while exhibiting intertrial variability. Furthermore, recent evidence suggests that skills involving environments in which objects within the performance environment move but at a constant speed and in the same spatial location can also be called closed skills. That is, the movements are organized similarly as long as no more than one dimension of the environment varies within a given trial (Gentile et al., 1975). In a task such as a shooting gallery, for example, the spatial dimension remains constant during the trial even though the target is moving.

Implicitly associated with spatial changes in the environment are temporal changes; any time there is a movement of an object in space both spatial and temporal changes occur. In the golf example, the spatial elements remain constant since there is no movement of the ball prior to the swing. The temporal elements are thus unimportant in terms of environmental regulation of movement since there is no time stress imposed.

The concepts of spatial and temporal elements are described separately in order to clarify our analysis of organized human movement. It must be emphasized that they are inextricably linked in the real-world environment. For the teacher, student, and researcher in motor skills, separation of spatial and temporal elements also aids in understanding the relative contribution of each to the organization of movement.

The spatial elements of the environment can vary in one, two, or three dimensions. When the spatial elements are one-dimensional the objects remain in a stationary position, as in golf or typing. The object remains stationary until acted upon by some form of external force. When the spatial elements are two-dimensional the objects are changing direction through only one plane of motion in space. (With reference to an earlier definition of planes of movement of the body this would be in either the frontal, sagittal, or horizontal plane.) An object may change position across the front of the performer or move directly toward or away from the performer. An example of this type of spatial element would be a shooting gallery where the moving targets travel in the same plane of reference, usually parallel to the frontal plane of the performer.

The spatial elements for many sports type activities are three-dimensional. The object moves through three planes simultaneously. For example, a pitched baseball on its approach toward the batter is simultaneously moving through three perpendicular planes of motion: frontal, sagittal, and horizontal. In the frontal plane the ball may be moving from left to right, at the same time it is moving toward the batter through the horizontal plane and dropping from a high delivery point to the region of the knees of the batter through the sagittal plane.

The temporal elements of the environment are continuous in only one dimension. As an object travels through space, the time from one point to another, or from one event to another, changes in only one dimension. For example, the time for an object to travel through space can vary from slow to fast. The baseball may be pitched fast or slow; the time it takes to reach the plate is the temporal element. It should now be more obvious that spatial elements and temporal elements can be separated only theoretically.

SPATIAL AND TEMPORAL ELEMENTS AS REGULATORY FACTORS: ENVIRONMENTAL CONSTRAINTS

With respect to the organization of movements and the relative effect of spatial versus temporal elements as regulators of movement, there is a practical reason to view spatial and temporal elements separately. It may well be that for certain tasks or skills the spatial elements play a more regulatory role than the temporal elements, and vice versa. Practically, the spatial elements of the performance environment refer to the *where*—where an object will appear or an event will occur in space. When referring to the temporal elements of the performance environment we are referring to the *when*—when an object will be at a particular location or when an event will occur in time.

An additional, but important temporal element, is *independent temporal control*. They are the go, stop, go-stop, and rhythmic elements that for certain tasks or skills have a regulatory influence upon our movements. These are based upon time and can be defined as the beginning of a movement (go), the termination of a movement or sequence of movements (stop), a period within which movements must be completed (go-stop), and a temporal pattern to which the movement must conform (rhythmic).

Because of their regulatory function in movement, rules and equipment are considered to be environmental constraints. Both rules and equipment design have elements of spatial and temporal control (and independent temporal control) functions and hence may also determine the spatial and temporal organization of the movement. (As will be seen in Chapter Eight, rules and equipment design can also be used as a means of compensating for morphologic constraints.)

By looking at any skill or task, we can determine in a subjective fashion which element, spatial or temporal, may perform the primary regulatory function. It is emphasized, however, that with respect to the organization of movements, *both spatial and temporal elements are regulatory*. Their regulatory influence may simply vary by degree.

When the outfielder in baseball goes for a high fly ball or a line drive, the spatial elements may be more regulatory than the temporal elements. The important factor in this case is to be in the correct spot and position, and then to be there at the right time. Being early, for example, would facilitate a more accurate and appropriate movement response but may not be the most important regulatory function. When batting, the temporal element may be more important or regulatory. Though the spatial element certainly exists, the fact that the spatial dimension is more restricted may make the "when to hit" more regulatory. This also has to do with overcoming the time lags inherent in the organism.[1] The batter, prior to swinging the bat, can predict within a fairly restricted range where the bat must go to be coincident with the ball. When to initiate the swing in order to be coincident with the pitched ball is more uncertain, and is thus a temporal regulatory control function.

In an activity such as swimming, the spatial and temporal elements of the performance environment are relatively stable. It is the independent temporal elements of the starter's gun, the rules, and the type of pool (size, lighting, etc.) that become the regulatory factors. Students might wish to think of other skills and analyze and describe their spatial and temporal elements as regulatory environmental constraints. This analysis of spatial and temporal elements is not in conflict with the motor skill classification system described in Chapter Two. It should instead provide the student with additional resolution when considering how the environment affects the regulation of movements classified according to the predictability of environmental events.

The examples just presented have shown how spatial and temporal elements in the environment might be regulatory for specific skills. This regulation is a form of environmental constraint to which our movements must be matched in order to accomplish goals. This regulation is important in terms of the predictability of the spatial and temporal elements of the environment.

ENVIRONMENTAL PREDICTABILITY

The relationship between spatial and temporal elements for any given environmental situation determines the degree to which the performer can predict their properties. The ability to predict the spatial and temporal elements regulates the performer's movements. Spatial and temporal elements interact continuously, and the relative regulatory influence of each defines a continuum of environmental regulation (certainty versus uncertainty of spatial and temporal elements). This continuum for spatial and temporal events has been described as ranging from predictability to unpredictability.

As environmental events become more and more predictable through practice and experience, the performer's ability successfully and effectively to accomplish the task improves. As the learner becomes familiar with the spatial and temporal configurations of the performance environment, these specific elements become redundant. Once redundancy for specific environmental events occurs, better and better predictions about the nature of the movement response are made. Redundancy and resulting improved predictability are what limits chaos in our movement organization (Howard and Templeton, 1966).

When the teacher or student is concerned with environmental constraints, the key factor relates to the predictability of spatial or temporal elements, or both, that will influence the organization of the movement. Depending upon the type of task and the nature of the environment, one practical form of analysis for the teacher to use might be to identify four possible categories of spatial and temporal regulation. The relative influence of spatial and temporal control will vary for each of the four categories along the described continuum. For some tasks and skills, one environmental element may be more important than another; for example, spatial elements may be the more important regulatory factor because of the change in position of objects in the environment, while temporal elements remain relatively constant. The four categories are as follows (the symbols "S" and "T" are used to describe each category; the capital letter designates the major regulatory function and lower-case letter designates minimal regulatory functions):

1. s/t: The regulatory demands provided by spatial and temporal elements are minimal. This type of control might be common in self-pacing motor acts such as writing or speech. (Biomechanical and morphologic constraints may be more influential as the regulatory parameters.)
2. S/t: The spatial elements of the environment are more regulatory than are the temporal elements. Skills or tasks labeled closed skills—golf, diving, high jump, gymnastics—are regulated by spatial components of the environment. The environment spatially restricts the movements, with little or no restriction imposed by temporal elements of the environment. The teacher will thus want to focus the student's attention on the predictable elements of the spatial environment since the temporal elements would not appear to have as strong an influence upon the organization of the movement.
3. s/T: The temporal elements of the environment are more regulatory than are the spatial elements. From trial to trial the temporal elements are less predictable, and to be effective the movement must match the temporal elements of the environment. Skills such as passing a football, throwing darts at a moving target (where the spatial position of the target is the same for each trial,

but its speed of movement varies), and batting a baseball are but a few examples of skills where the temporal aspects of the environment appear to play the more regulatory function.

4. S/T: Spatial and temporal elements within the environment provide an equally regulatory function upon the organization of the movement. Space and time are varying to such a degree that the predictability of events within the environment is relatively low. Movement must conform to both spatial and temporal elements. Skills such as tennis, badminton, and walking along a sidewalk crowded with people are but a few examples of motor skills for which spatial and temporal elements are equally regulatory.

Students will want to select a variety of skills and attempt to identify the regulatory environmental components (s/t, S/t, s/T, S/T) for each. The related role of independent temporal control should also receive consideration. In addition to identifying the spatial and temporal components for each skill, consideration also needs to be given to the relative importance of each element early in practice versus late in practice. The regulatory influence of each element may change as the level of performance improves. Analysis of movement for any selected skill involves the need for understanding the regulatory environmental conditions.

MOVEMENTS AND THE ENVIRONMENT

Movements are performed within our environment, under environmental, biomechanical, and morphologic regulation, and in time and space. Movements, as we have seen, usually have an effect upon the environment—whether to perform for aesthetic reasons, to express feeling or emotion, or to complete some kind of task or sports skill. It is therefore necessary to consider spatial and temporal components of the movement.

Since the regulatory conditions of the environment have such a profound effect upon the organization of our movements, it seems reasonable to assume that there will be a spatial and temporal relationship between the environment and the movement. This has been called the "environmental dependency concept" (Bernstein, 1967; Gentile, 1972). The environmental dependency concept suggests that the environmental performance context provides the regulatory function to which movements must be matched in time and space; that is, movements must be organized spatially and temporally to conform to environmental conditions.

When the environmental demands are more spatial, the movement will be organized so that the resultant action appears behaviorally to exhibit consistent spatial parameters. When the environmental demands are more temporal, the movement will be organized so that the resultant action appears behaviorally to exhibit corresponding temporal parameters; that is, timing a throw or timing the release of an object become critical movement factors. In environments in which the spatial and temporal elements vary together, a correspondingly different population of movements is produced, each related to the environmental characteristics (Gentile, 1975; Higgins and Spaeth, 1972; Spaeth, 1973). The time available to the performer for monitoring the environment, organizing the response, and executing the response can be a severely limiting feature of skills performed under these conditions (S/T). In large part this involves overcoming the time lags inherent in the system and is accomplished by predicting the "nature of subsequent environmental situations" and organizing and executing the movement accordingly (Spaeth, 1973:8).

As the spatial and temporal demands of the environment increase, the performer must develop a repertoire of movements appropriate to each possible environmental condition (S/T combination); that is, for movements to match environmental conditions, which may change from trial to trial, the performer must vary the movement to correspond to the spatial and temporal dimensions of the environment. The evolving pattern of movement for any task is therefore a function of the interaction between the degree of environmental change and the complexity of the movement itself.

Again, students and teachers interested in analysis of movement should give attention to the spatial and temporal elements regulating movements and to the corresponding spatial and temporal components of the movement itself. To aid in this analysis the following questions might be asked about any skill chosen:

1. What is the present level of skill being observed?
2. What are the regulatory spatial and temporal elements of the environment? (Describe each.)
3. What are the spatial and temporal parameters of the movement that can be observed? (Describe each.)
4. What is the relationship between spatial and temporal elements of the environment and the movement?
5. What changes in spatial and temporal relationships between environment and movement can be observed?

In conclusion, the environment provides information to the performer, and through the self-regulating system (CNS) the performer must program the appropriate movement response. The environment's role has its effect in the past, largely because of the ability of the performer to make predictions about future events based upon past events (or points in time). Our movements are patterned according to the way the world appears to exist spatially and temporally and the way the body is constructed. For effective goal accomplishment, our movement repertoire, our behavior, must match the constraints imposed by our environment, our morphology, and the related biomechanical factors.

NOTES

1. Time lags are dealt with as morphologic constraints because they are considered information-processing factors and perceptual processes. For now we will say only that time lags refer to the time it takes to gather environmental information, process that information, and initiate the required movements for completing the task.

SEVEN

Biomechanical constraints and organized human movement

Purposeful human movement involves overcoming the external forces impinging upon the system. Furthermore, it involves the application of certain physical or mechanical principles in order to overcome these imposed forces. Along with meeting the constraints imposed by the environment and the morphology, the skilled performer—in sport, dance, or the industrial setting—is also limited by the ability to deal with independent forces such as gravity, mass, and inertia. In Chapter Three these independent forces were referred to as the "peripheral mechanical source of variation affecting the pattern of movement." The biomechanical constraints imposed upon the moving organism can in essence form the subgoals of many motor skills or tasks, often an extremely important and essential concomitant of skilled performance.

The long jumper may have two subgoals with which to contend during each performance. These subgoals are the exact placement of the jumping foot on the take-off board and the generation of maximum force at a specific point in the movement. As previously indicated, there are two important biomechanical factors that may form subgoals for the performer. These factors can now be identified as biomechanical constraints that are believed to play an essential role in the acquisition of skill. *Biomechanical constraints are the independent physical forces, such as gravity, mass, and inertia, that impose themselves upon the organization of the movement.*

In order to produce an appropriate pattern of movement for the successful accomplishment of a particular goal, it is necessary for the performer to overcome these biomechanical constraints, the independent, external forces. For example, specific biomechanical constraints are explicitly important subgoals when learning, among other skills, to throw a ball, to clear the high bar in track, or to perform a kip in gymnastics. Without some notion of the mechanical principles involved in a particular activity, the teacher may encounter difficulty in analyzing a student's performance or describing or explaining the movement and hence in facilitating the acquisition of the skill. Conversely, the students, left to their own design, may lose a great deal of time through trial-and-error practice in achieving the goal. When a biomechanical constraint is synthesized in such a way as to identify specific physical principles of movement, we can say it is a construct. Constructs, for our purposes, can be identified as subgoals of a task or skill. The constructs presented in this chapter form a concomitant part of the goal of the movement or skill and hence need identification and explanation.

Overcoming external forces such as gravity and inertia is an important part of the self-regulatory system. Understanding the principles and constructs involved is therefore relevant when studying organized, purposeful human movement.

A construct is an idea or image constructed from a synthesis of related parts. A *biomechanical construct*[1] is the result of the synthesis of knowledge and subject matter related to constraints imposed upon the moving system by gravity, mass and inertia. Fig. 7-1 schematically identifies four basic biomechanical constructs and their relationship to the organization of movement: (1) summation of internal forces, (2) receiving and impart-

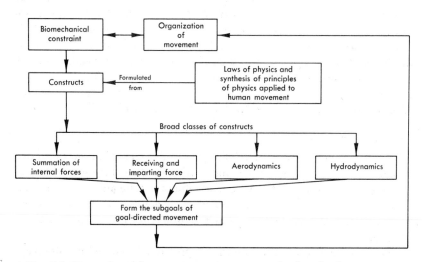

Fig. 7-1. Biomechanical constraints, constructs, and subgoals of movement.

ing force, (3) aerodynamic action of projectiles, and (4) hydrodynamics, or fluid mechanics (Logan and McKinney, 1970). These constructs are abstracted primarily from the basic laws of physics formulated in the eighteenth century by Sir Isaac Newton. Taken by themselves, these laws are easily understood by anyone who has had a high school physics course. The application of the laws to the practical solution of movement problems is somewhat more difficult. These constructs have been formulated in order to aid the teacher in the identification of subgoals of a task or skill. In addition, they represent an important basis for thinking about analysis of movement in both a qualitative and a quantitative sense. For a more detailed treatment of the biomechanics of sports skills the reader is referred to Hay (1973) and Northrup et al. (1974).

REVIEW OF THREE BASIC LAWS FROM PHYSICS
Law of inertia

The law of inertia states that a body will remain at rest or in uniform motion until acted upon by an external force that brings about a change in the existing state of the body. *Inertia* is that property of matter that makes it resist a change in motion; it is often used interchangeably with mass. *Mass* is the measure of an object's inertia, the measured resistance of an object to change in motion. *Momentum* is the product of mass and velocity.

In order to project the body upward, as in a simple vertical jump, forces of a magnitude sufficient to overcome the inertia of the body must be generated. A corollary to this law states that to change direction of a moving object a force must be applied. For example, in order to change direction of a hockey puck the performer must in some way apply a new force in a different direction—in the direction of the intended path of the puck. A final corollary deals with the fact that a body will remain in motion until acted upon by an external force. Friction (air and ground) is of course one means by which a body's motion is decreased. When catching a ball the force is often in the form of controlled muscular contractions offering increasing resistance to the momentum of the ball.

Law of acceleration

The law of acceleration states that the rate of change in momentum is proportional to the force exerted and to the direction of the applied force. Acceleration is the rate of change of an object in time and space, the rate at which the velocity of a moving object is changing. *Velocity* is the speed of an object, measured by the distance an object travels in a known period of time.

When a force of some magnitude is applied to a body with some mass, the body will change its speed in relation to the magnitude of the force. In other words, when a baseball, which has a given mass, is thrown, the rate of change of speed of the ball is proportional to the magnitude of force generated. This will be of particular importance when dealing with principles relating to summation of internal forces. Increased application of force can be achieved through successively applying the forces generated in successive body and limb segments or by increasing muscular force or both.

Law of reaction

The law of reaction states that for every action there is an equal and opposite reaction. A force exerted by an object against another results in the production of an equal and opposite force. This might be conceived of as a kind of force interaction where there is an interaction of forces between, for example, body parts, instruments, objects, or surfaces. A classic example of this law is demonstrated in locomotion on two types of surface. When walking on the sidewalk the force of the ground pushes back with equal and opposite force due to excessive mass of the earth, thus aiding the body's forward movement. The friction created by the foot's contact with the ground makes this force interaction possible. In contrast, when walking on smooth ice, the foot pushes backward, but due to lack of friction there is no opposite reaction, and the body—with respect to locomotion—remains in one place, spinning one's wheels as it were, and going nowhere. The body remains in place provided the performer maintains muscular control.

Another example of this concept occurs in the situation where the performer jumps from a high diving board. If the legs are thrust forward during the course of the free fall towards the water, the body rotates backward.

Assuming the presence of adequate friction, when the body is supported the reaction force propels the body in an opposite direction with equal force. In human movement we deal with a series of rigid bodies and hence there is some loss of force due to the body's absorbing force in its soft tissue. When a body is unsupported, as in free fall in skydiving or jumping from a diving board, the body itself must contend with and absorb the reaction force in order to control the movement.

The application of this law is most important when considering activities involving projection and control of the body in space, such as gymnastics, tumbling, and diving stunts.

Together these three laws provide the basic underlying theoretical support for the following biomechanical constructs.

BIOMECHANICAL CONSTRUCT DEALING WITH SUMMATION OF INTERNAL FORCES

The construct of the summation of internal forces is a most important one for the teacher of motor skill. All coordinated movement activity has as one of its basic elements the effective application of muscular force through successive body and limb segments in time and space. By summation of internal forces, we mean the application or maximization of generated muscular force at the point of impact, point of greatest strength, or point of most accuracy within a kinematic chain of movement. The direct result of coordinated musculoskeletal action—moving the body segments in a desired, effective, efficient fashion—demands combining the movement of successively arranged links into a goal-directed movement. The combination of successively linked segments of the kinematic chain provides the precision, accuracy, consistency, and maximum force that constitutes a skilled movement. In essence this involves the effective summation of the degrees of freedom of motion in a kinematic chain through regulated muscular force and skeletal action.

Ergonomic cycle in summation of internal forces

We shall view the summation of internal forces as related to the whole movement, that is, the beginning, middle, and end of a goal-directed movement. The field of study historically called ergonomics, which deals with human work efficiency and time-motion study, provides a simple, clear, time-tested method of breaking down the whole movement. The whole movement is described as an ergonomic cycle, defined for a particular task or skill, and is the total movement needed to complete the task. For convenience of study, this cycle is arbitrarily partitioned into three phases of movement—the preparation, the operation (or action), and the return (or follow-through). These three phases are of major importance when discussing certain types of descriptive and measurement tools used for the analysis of movement. The *preparation* stage involves readying the moving system (the links and the body or postural support system) for the action. The *operation*, or *action*, stage is that portion of the total movement directly related to the accomplishment of the task. The *return*, or *follow-through*, stage returns the body to the preliminary position or state. There are no distinct lines of demarcation between these phases; instead each phase represents a rather arbitrary section within the ergonomic cycle. Each phase will very often represent a specific organizational factor. For example, the preparation phase may be of primary importance because it places the limbs and body in an advantageous position for the action phase of the movement. As in the baseball swing or tennis stroke, the body may be rotated and the limbs brought back for the purpose of achieving maximum range of motion. This results in increased generation of force and speed of movement for two reasons: (1) the muscles responsible for the action are put on greater stretch, which allows for the generation of greater contractile power because they can contract over a greater distance, and (2) body and limb segments can be successively brought into action over a greater distance beginning with the large postural segments and ending with the limb segments involved.

Within the ergonomic cycle for a particular task or skill, each individual has a unique line of motion, or pattern of movement, with which he is most comfortable.

Coordinated movement thus involves adding the required amount of articular movement for each successive segment to form a smooth ergonomic cycle. The goal of the movement may be to generate maximum speed, distance, or force of the body, limbs, or external objects. Each participating link must be brought into a movement at precisely the right

Table 3. Biomechanical goal of movement and summation of internal forces

Biomechanical goal of the movement	Related biomechanical principles associated with construct of summation of internal forces
Production of accuracy	Stable basis of support Stable body support system Use of distal limb segments and associated limb segments Consistency of pattern of movement
Production of speed	Successive generation of speed in each link Small initial radius in kinematic chain All participating muscles or muscle groups begin contraction from maximum length possible
Production of force	Successive use of segments from initiation of movement to termination (through action phase) Summation of muscle force transferred from large to small muscles through action phase Stable base of support: wide base, lowered center of gravity Application of movement generated force in desired direction
Production of force to project an external object	Stable base of support necessary for maximization of force generation and control of direction Greatest stability achieved when base of support is close to body center of gravity. Lower center of gravity increases stability at base of support Greater the weight of projected object in relation to performer, the more important is maintaining foot contact with base of support and generating force and speed of movement through successive muscle-limb involvement

point in time and space in order to smoothly, efficiently, and effectively accomplish the goal. The movement of the arm and wrist of someone learning to throw a ball often seem to be out of sequence with each other and with the body itself. In this instance, precision, accuracy, consistency, and maximum force do not seem to be achieved.

Within the ergonomic cycle, several principles that relate to the summation of internal forces can be identified. Table 3 depicts four biomechanical goals of the movement and outlines the principles related to the summation of internal forces required to accomplish the respective biomechanical goal. The four biomechanical goals of the movement are as follows: (1) movements for production of accuracy, (2) movements for the production of speed, (3) movements for production of maximum force, and (4) movements for production of forces to project external objects.

Transfer of force and speed to succeeding segments

In general movements, whether for generation of force, generation of speed, achievement of accuracy, or all three, begin at a point relatively proximal to the midline of the body. As the cycle of the movement progresses, the more distal links successively come into action. The large muscles associated with body support and body transport produce the initial movement action. Movements for body support and transport use muscles of power. Such muscles are shorter and thicker than muscles associated with speed, accuracy, and limb manipulation. MacConaill and Basmajian (1969) refer to these as "spurt" muscles, or muscles that produce acceleration directly along the angle of motion between any two segments. "A markedly spurt-type muscle is biomechanically the most suitable for starting and maintaining motion of a bone at a joint" (MacConaill and Basmajian, 1969:112).

Progressing distally toward the extremities, the segments and muscles are longer and have increasingly larger central nervous system representation. This would imply that as the movement progresses greater speed and increased accuracy is achieved. The increase in speed occurs because the force of a contracting muscle is applied over a greater distance due to the length of the segment and hence the muscle; increased accuracy occurs because of the increased ratio of innervation for muscle and motoneuron. For example, the muscles of the wrist and the hand have fewer muscle fibers associated with each motor neuron than do those in the muscles of the shoulder girdle. Furthermore, the hand has a much greater representation area within the motor cortex than does the upper arm. MacConaill and Basmajian (1969) would classify muscles of the above description as "shunt" muscles. A shunt muscle "acts chiefly during rapid movement and along the long axis of the moving bone to provide centripetal force" (MacConaill and Basmajian, 1969:114).[2]

Prior to the initiation of the action phase of the movement, the participating segments are moved into the position of readiness. During this preparation phase the muscles that initiate and carry out the action phase are placed in a position of stretch. This allows the participating muscles to contract over a greater distance and hence to apply muscular force over a greater distance. *The force exerted by a muscle or group of muscles is directly proportional to muscle length.* An increase in muscle length results in more force or speed generation, or both, for the limb. With the successive transfer of movement from the larger power muscles located more proximally to the midline of the body to the longer, thinner muscles, a transfer of force to speed is achieved, resulting in movement through the successive segments to the termination of the action phase. The generated force, therefore, is transferred from the larger, stronger muscles to the smaller, longer muscles. The velocity generated by each participating segment exceeds the velocity of each preceding segment.

To achieve maximum speed of movement of a limb or projectile, the successive summation of segments must obviously generate maximum speed. For those movements requiring maximum speed, this involves initiating the movement of the kinematic chain with as short a radius as possible. When we throw, the movement begins in the trunk and is transferred to the upper arm through the shoulder girdle and then to the lower arm, wrist, hand, and fingers. Speed of movement can be more rapidly generated when the limbs are drawn in close to the body and only successively brought into action during the course of the whole movement. This is a kind of cracking of the whip action. Toyoshima et al. (1974) have shown, for example, that the speed of a thrown ball is the result not only of the speed of the arm at the elbow but more importantly of the speed of rotation of the body. More than 50% of the speed of the thrown ball can be accounted for by the rotation of the body.

During the follow-through phase, the successive segments are decelerated until they are brought into the original position or a new position in possible preparation for the next movement. The muscles having the greater power, the spurt muscles, begin the deceleration process; the longer, weaker muscles, the shunt muscles, act over a longer period of time and provide the precision for the final position. The follow-through phase is usually smooth in order to prepare for the next movement.

This concept of transfer of force and speed to succeeding segments is especially significant to our thinking about coordination and regulation of movement. For example, if we generate power and stability from those segments and muscles located more proximally, it would follow that perhaps the organization of the movement begins with the body support system. The programming of movements of support and stability subsequently leads to the programming of the limb manipulation movements that achieve the precision and accuracy in our movement repertoire (Higgins, 1972). This is especially tenable when we look at the development of a child's movement repertoire. Here we see the body support functions—the larger, more gross movements responsible for locomotion, postural support, and large limb movements—developing first, followed by the more precise and accurate functions such as grasping.

Application of maximum force and speed in an intended direction

Another factor important in coordinated motor acts is the application of the maximum force possible in precisely the correct direction and at the correct moment. It was suggested earlier that a subgoal in the long jump was to apply the maximum amount of force against the take-off board at the correct moment in time and space. In addition, it is important to apply this maximum amount of force in the correct direction. If the jumper generated the maximum take-off force in a vertical direction, his resulting jump would not achieve the maximum distance for the force generated; much of the force would be generated in a direction counterproductive to the task.

The guiding principle here is that *for maximum force and speed in a movement, the sum of the forces of successive segments should be applied in the direction of the intended movement.* If we wish to complete the long jump with the maximum distance, the movement of successive limb segments must be accomplished in such a way as to produce their maximum force in the direction of the intended motion. Theoretically, the action phase of the movement should terminate by projecting the center of gravity of the body off the take-off board at an angle of 45 degrees.

The shot-put can provide another interesting example. The goal of this activity is to project a heavy sphere over a maximum distance. Achieving maximum distance requires as much force as possible to be generated by the muscular system and applied in exactly the correct direction. Again, this is achieved through summing the generated forces throughout the movement and applying these forces and generated speed in the optimal direction. A study of the evolution of the modern shot-put is illuminating. During the middle and late 1950s several shot-putters, led by Perry O'Brian, revolutionized the sport and rewrote the record books. Their breakthrough was largely the result of a change in the initial body position and movement across the ring. The new body position and approach allowed the putter to generate greater speed of movement over a greater period of time and position the body in such a fashion that the direction of the application of forces to the projectile was optimized. Instead of standing and facing the direction of the throw, the new style called for the performer to begin in a crouched and coiled position with his back toward the direction of the throw. The throw was initiated by movement across the ring and a simultaneous unwinding of the torso in order to bring the body into a position facing the direction of the throw. By the time the performer reached the opposite side of the ring, his body and limbs were fully extended in the direction of the throw. Hence, the summation of forces had been maximized because of the successive involvement of each part and the longer distance through which the forces could be applied.

Base of support, body center of gravity, and summation of internal forces

Body stability is necessary for the optimum and effective generation of force and direction control, both of the body itself and of external objects. The center of gravity of the body is a theoretical point at which all the weight (the force of gravity) may be considered to be concentrated; it is the point "about which a body or object would balance most perfectly" (Northrup et al., 1974:81). It is a variable point and is dependent upon the type of body, position of the body, and type of body movement. As a rule of thumb, the center of gravity of the body in an erect posture with arms at the sides lies roughly in the upper region of the pelvic girdle. Some estimates place it at a point 56% of an individual's height measured from the floor (Davidovits, 1975:3). The center of gravity of the body moves as if all the mass of the body were concentrated at that point. Each link or segment of the body has its own center of gravity, which is usually located along the longitudinal axis and relatively nearer to the proximal end of the bone.

When a force from outside or inside the body acts upon the body (through the center of gravity) it effects a translatory motion. A force acting upon the body through a point other than the center of gravity effects a rotational motion.

The *base of support* is the area included by the body contact with the supporting surface, usually through the feet. The base of support is stabilized by maintaining a vertical center of gravity as near as possible to the base, that is, a low center of gravity. In addition, for actions such as locomotion, diving, and certain gymnastic stunts, a position of instability is often desirable in order to facilitate the initiation of the movement. (This is why locomotion is defined as "purposeful maladjustment of the body." In effect, walking and running involve an interaction between a shifting base of support and a constantly falling center of gravity.) When the body is moving, the center of gravity is constantly shifting, thus requiring a constant shift in base of support in order to keep it under the center of gravity.

Some skills require a change in direction of movement at a point in time and space before the movement sequence (ergonomic cycle) has been completed. Base of support plays a vital role in actions involving changing direction, quick stopping, and receiving external force. Under normal conditions, the base of support is widened in order to lower the center of gravity and thus produce greater body stability. When the base of support is widened, control or change of direction is more easily achieved since the mass is distributed over a greater area.

Activities such as jumping for height—as in high jump, volleyball spike, jump shot in basketball—require that the initial horizontal momentum generated by the run be translated into a vertical motion. Again, the base of support is widened in order to permit sudden transla-tion of momentum from the horizontal to the vertical. With a widened base of support the center of gravity will naturally be lowered; this ac-complishes at once stability and a more desirable body position through which the vertical forces can be applied. As the actual translation from horizontal momentum to vertical momentum begins, the center of gravity will actually fall slightly behind the base of support. This shift of center of gravity from forward of the body to slightly behind compensates for the forward momentum and aids in the translation from the horizontal to vertical direction. Both the direction and the force of the jump are the result of summing the horizontally generated momentum of the run and the direction and magnitude of the force created by the actual push-off from the base of support. The entire horizontal momentum is not trans-lated into the momentum of the vertical portion of jump because the angle of the take-off force is somewhat in the opposite direction from the angle of the run. As in the high jump, jumps whose goal is to achieve maximum height can benefit by a slight forward running approach.

BIOMECHANICAL CONSTRUCT DEALING WITH AERODYNAMICS

Aerodynamics is a branch of dynamics that deals with the forces acting upon bodies in motion in space, influenced by the motion of air. In the study of skill and human movement, aerodynamics deals with the charac-teristics of projectiles, such as the flight of a ball in space or the flight pattern and movements as the body travels through space. This discus-sion will not relate to the interesting topic of flight of bodies in a weight-less, or nongravity, environment; see Howard and Templeton (1966) and Tricker and Tricker (1967) for excellent treatments of this topic. Our consideration will be limited to a brief statement of several principles that relate to the flight patterns of objects projected in space, the flight pattern of the body in space, and the reaction of an object when it strikes a rigid surface. Space is operationally defined as the area near the surface of the earth where gravity is maximally effective.

In general, the flight of objects in space is affected by direct external forces such as gravity, air resistance, humidity, temperature, barometric pressure, and altitude. Practically, some of these external forces are negligible, while others, such as gravity, have a major effect on flight pattern. In addition, the shape and surface texture of a projected object are important influences upon its flight pattern. For example, air resistance is an important factor for consideration in the design of the javilin and the golf ball. The flight characteristics of a tennis ball are dependent upon its surface texture as well as its angle and velocity of projection. Those of a new, fuzzy ball are different from those of an old smooth ball. These are important considerations for the teacher who is attempting to provide an optimal learning environment for the facilitation of skill. For example, it may not be advisable to provide smooth, worn-out tennis balls for practice.

Flight pattern of an object projected in space

The optimum angle for projecting an object into space is dependent upon the goal of the task or skill and the physical characteristics of the projected object. For example, we may want to achieve maximum distance, as in the shot-put and javelin throw, maximum speed and accuracy, as in baseball pitching and tennis serving, or maximum height, as in a lob shot in tennis or badminton. The flight path of an object's center of gravity is determined primarily by the angle of projection and to some extent by the physical characteristics of the object. Once an object is in free flight, having left the projecting surface, be it a hand, the ground, or a racket, the path in space scribed by its center of gravity will not change. The law of inertia discussed earlier, indicates that only change in the path of the object's center of gravity would have to be brought about by the action of a new external force, such as, for example, by striking a baseball or a tennis ball.

Since gravity (and to a certain extent friction created against the object by the air in our immediate space) is acting upon all projected objects, they will describe a path similar in shape to a parabola, an inverted U (Fig. 7-2). Fig. 7-2 also demonstrates that the flight path is more acute during descent than ascent. This is due to the effect of air resistance, which decreases the velocity of the object. From the performer's point of view when reacting to an object in flight, this decrease in velocity of the object is probably only theoretical.

In Fig. 7-2 the theoretical path of the center of gravity of a projectile is illustrated for several angles of projection with the same amount of projective force for each angle. Observe that there is an optimal angle of projection or take-off for achieving either maximum height or maximum distance. Fig. 7-2, *A*, shows an angle of take-off approximating the vertical; the horizontal distance achieved by the projectile is minimal but the height achieved is greater than in the other examples. Fig. 7-2, *E*, shows

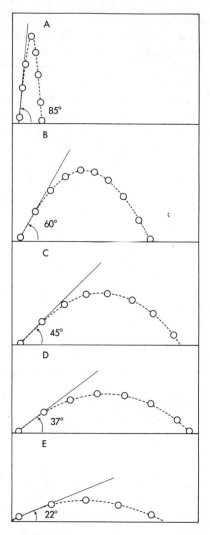

Fig. 7-2. Flight path of a ball projected at varying angles with equal force.

a low angle of projection where neither maximum height nor distance is achieved. In Fig. 7-2, *C*, the angle of projection is approximately 40 degrees and results in the maximum distance. The angles of projection in *B* and *D* produce lesser distances than that in *C*. "Maximum range was obtained in that case for an angle of projection of about 40°. The angle depends upon the ratio of the force applied to the weight of the ball. The smaller the force of projection the lower is the angle required to achieve maximum range" (Tricker and Tricker, 1967:114).

The height achieved by a projected object is proportional to the velocity at the point of release and inversely proportional to air resistance. For practical purposes air resistance is negligible for spherical objects; however, it becomes more important for objects of uneven shape. For the performer, therefore, velocity at point of projection, speed of movement, and angle of projection are the primary factors under direct control when projecting objects in space. Once an object has been projected into space, movement around its center of gravity will not change its flight pattern. The weight of an object traveling in space exerts a downward vertical force and therefore weight will alter only the vertical momentum of the object. The horizontal momentum is thus unaltered (Tricker and Tricker, 1967). The downward trend of the object in Fig. 7-2 illustrates this principle.

Flight pattern of the body in space

The flight of the body in space involves three basic types of situations: the achievement of height, as in the high jump and the rebound in basketball, the achievement of distance, as in the long jump, and rotational movements in space, as in diving and tumbling. For achievement of greatest height, the forces projecting the center of gravity must be applied as nearly as possible in a vertical direction. In the projection of the body into space, whether for height or for distance, the problem is to translate linear momentum from body transport and rotational momentum from limb movements into vertical momentum. When high jumping or spiking a volleyball, one increases the height of the jump by an initially small body transport movement producing the linear momentum. The horizontal momentum is translated into vertical momentum as a result of four factors: widened base of support and hence lowered center of gravity just prior to take-off; lowered center of gravity allowed to fall slightly behind the base of support, creating a pendulum effect facilitating the transfer of linear momentum to vertical momentum; application of muscular force directed as nearly as possible through the center of gravity; and vertical direction of forces generated by the rotational movement of individual limb segments.

In skills such as the long jump, the performer must first determine the optimal trajectory of the center of gravity in order to project the body through space so that the heels will land a maximum distance from the take-off board. Basically, for the long jumper the task is to convert linear momentum, generated from the run, into distance. The jump itself involves carrying the "center of gravity up and over the feet" in order to free the feet from the ground and move them forward in preparation for the landing beyond the theoretical landing point of the center of gravity (Tricker and Tricker, 1967). The performer has available a number of styles of jumping to attain height or distance; the basic principles for jumping remain the same.

When projecting the body into space, whether for height, distance, or some other performance task such as diving or tumbling, the center of gravity of the body will describe a path similar to that described for such objects as a tennis ball or volleyball (Fig. 7-2). The path described is a function of both angle of projection and velocity at take-off. The path of the center of gravity cannot be altered once the feet have left the supporting surface, such as the diving board or floor.

Certain rotational actions of the limbs, such as twists, spins, and somersaults, can be accomplished once the performer is in space; however, these rotational movements do not change the path of the center of gravity. The flight pattern of the body in space is therefore a function of angle of projection at take-off, velocity at take-off, and the nature and goal of the task or skill.

Reaction of an object when contacting rebound surface

The angle of rebound of objects is an important factor in many sport skills, such as tennis, handball, squash, and badminton. The angle of rebound of objects from a solid surface is directly related to the angle of approach of the object. In addition, the angle of rebound is dependent upon the direction of rotation of the object as it contacts the rebounding surface (Cooper and Glassow, 1976; Logan and McKinney, 1970). For example, if a ball contacts the rebound surface at an angle of 45 degrees with no spin, it will rebound at an angle of 45 degrees. If the ball is spinning upon contact with the rebound surface, the rebound will be in the direction of the spin.

BIOMECHANICAL CONSTRUCT DEALING WITH HYDRODYNAMICS

Hydrodynamics deals with the movement of an object through water and the external forces that affect this movement. The movement of the body through water is primarily a problem of dealing with buoyancy, water resistance, and the propulsive body forces against a relatively unstable medium. In locomotion on the land (walking and running), our actions must overcome or use the effect of gravity. In swimming, however, the effects of gravity are negligible; buoyancy is the primary factor to be contended with. *Buoyancy* is the tendency of an object to float when submerged in a fluid; it is the upward force exerted by the fluid upon a submerged object. A person's ability to float is largely a function of morphologic constraints, the structural composition of the bones, muscles, body fat, and connective tissue. The greater the density of body composition the less buoyant the performer.

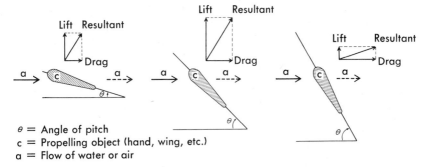

θ = Angle of pitch
c = Propelling object (hand, wing, etc.)
a = Flow of water or air

Fig. 7-3. Lift-drag interaction and resultant force involved in moving through water or air.

Movement through the water, therefore, becomes a problem of over-coming the effects of buoyancy and water resistance. The propulsive forces generated by the body and limbs are applied against a fluid sub-stance that offers less resistance than the solid surface of a playing field. These factors are constraints upon the organization of movement in the water (Fig. 7-3).

The performer's subgoal in the case of swimming would be to apply forces, through appropriate muscular contraction and limb and body posi-tion control, in such a fashion as to match the constraints imposed by the environment, in this case the resistance of the water. For example, recent evidence has shown that in the crawl stroke in swimming, pulling the arm and hand straight back in line with the direction of movement forward does not maximize the application of force to produce the most speed forward (Schleihauf, 1974). The crawl stroke swimmer needs to move the hand in such a manner as to create maximal forward lift force. Counsilman (1968) and Schleihauf (1974, 1976) both point out that this forward lift force is achieved through a sculling motion of the hand. It is a motion that moves either up and down or side to side in a kind of undulating or figure-eight pattern, depending upon the stroke. It is important to note that this notion is an application of the Bernouli principle, which in fluid mechanics and aerodynamics explains Newton's law of action-reaction. It is the differential of pressure, high on one side of the hand and low on the other side, that produces the lift. The sculling motion achieves increased velocity of the hand in the water. This in turn produces a greater force differential between the palm of the hand and the back of the hand, which results in a high positive forward lift force. The swimmer must therefore be able to continuously alter the pitch[3] of the hand in accordance with the progress of the stroke through the water. There is an optimal pitch of the hand that will maximize the lift force. When there is too much pitch the hand is acting as a paddle; with too little pitch the hand simply slides through the water. "Thus we see that in order to produce maximum lift forces a swimmer must strike a delicate balance in hand pitch based on his sensitivity or feel for the water" (Schleihauf, 1974).

The lift force is not the only biomechanical factor that must be dealt with by the swimming mechanics of the performer. The lift force produces the vertical component of the propulsive force. There is also a horizontal component, called *drag*. The drag force is created by the flow of water around the hand. The drag force component impedes speed and accounts for much of the resistance to progress through both water and air (Hay, 1973). Drag is dependent upon velocity, surface area, smoothness of the surface, and the medium involved (Hay, 1973). The drag and lift force components act at right angles to each other. The resultant of these two forces produces the actual propulsion of the body through the water. In swimming and other activities in which hydrodynamic and aerodynamic principles apply there is an interaction between the drag and lift forces. In swimming, in sailing, in the flight of an airplane or a discus, "the lift and drag force components entirely determine the orientation of the resultant propulsive force" (Schleihauf, 1974). As the pitch increases the relationship between lift and drag components changes, which effects the resultant force or effective propulsive force (Fig. 7-3).

The following six principles from hydrodynamics relate to overcoming those constraints imposed by movement of the body through water:

1. Propulsive forces must be continuously applied or the body will not remain in motion.
2. Propulsive forces are generated most effectively by a sculling type motion where an optimal and continuous pitch can be applied against the resistance created by the water.
3. Maximum propulsive force is achieved by presenting as broad a surface area as possible to the water. Pressure exerted by a body part against the water produces movement in the opposite direction; thus, pushing downward in the water tends to push the body upward, and vice versa. To optimize the body movement for forward propulsion, coordinated limb and body movements must act so as to place the propelling surface at the pitch that results in a maximum lift force component and a minimal drag force component.
4. Application of propulsive force must be properly timed and sequentially ordered and summed. When this does not occur, counterforces—eddies and low pressure areas causing drag—will retard the desired movement.
5. As propulsive force is applied to the water, the speed of movement

through the water will gradually increase until a point is reached where water resistance due to friction equals the applied forces.

6. To maximize the propulsive forces against the water, the larger muscle groups stabilize the body position and initiate the arm and leg actions. The smaller muscle groups continue the motion and maintain a streamlined effect of the extremities as they enter, move, and leave the water. When kicking in the crawl stroke, for example, the large extensor and flexor muscles of the hips provide the propulsive force that moves the leg. The smaller muscles of the legs remain relatively relaxed so that a slight undulating motion is generated from the knee through the ankle and the foot. The maintenance of a streamlined leg is accomplished by the smaller muscles.

The basic mechanical constraints have been reviewed in this chapter. This discussion is by no means exhaustive. The student is encouraged to seek more information and in-depth treatments of the subject matter presented. In terms of the organization of movement, biomechanical constraints interrelate with the environmental and morphologic constraints. The separation of pure biomechanical constraints from constraints of environment and morphology is difficult, and hence much of our thinking and study needs to be directed toward understanding this interrelationship. Identification of the biomechanical constructs and the related constraints should aid us in determining which factors are invariant and which are variant in the organization of our movements.

NOTES

1. The first authors to use the construct approach were Logan and McKinney (1970). Their term is "kinesiological construct."
2. Centripetal and centrifugal force are associated with angular kinetics. Both of these "forces are exerted whenever a body moves on a curved path" (Hay, 1973:169). *Centripetal force* acts toward the center of a rotating body; *centrifugal force* acts away from the center of a rotating body.
3. Pitch is defined as the angle made by the object (in this example, the hand) around its transverse axis.

EIGHT

Morphologic constraints and their significance in the organization of movement

Morphologic constraints—anatomic structure or function relationships—have traditionally been viewed as one of the central foci in the study of biomechanics. Morphologic constraints impose themselves upon the moving organism in a variety of ways. This chapter considers some of the more important morphologic constraints that students, teachers, and researchers concerned with skill and analysis of human movement will find useful. We begin by emphasizing that the morphology of the human organism must be viewed as part of a whole interactive process leading to organized, coordinated human movement.

In Fig. 4-2, four types of morphologic constraint were outlined: structural, functional, perceptual, and organismic. As will be seen, there is an inherent interrelationship between these factors. However, for ease of presentation and discourse and within the process-oriented approach, separate discussion of these constraints helps to elucidate their ultimate influence upon human movement.

The organization of movement entails compensating for specific unique morphologic characteristics and factors. The analysis of human movement deals with a variable system—that of the morphology. The body is made up of a variety of irregularly shaped bones, muscles, and other supporting tissue. The shape and make-up of the morphology is constantly changing from birth to death. There is, no doubt, a more stable period following adolescence during which little if any growth and little if any deterioration occurs. This is roughly the period of young adulthood and probably reflects that stage in one's life where physical performance reaches its peak and during which the patterns of movement become increasingly consistent. With aging, or following physical injury, a change in morphology often is associated with a related change in the pattern of movement. Each irregularity within the morphologic system has a unique influence upon the movements of each individual performer. The dynamic features of our movements are dictated by the imposed morphologic constraints (Gagne and Fleishman, 1959). *Dynamic features* are the spatial and temporal dimensions of the performing environment.

TYPES OF MORPHOLOGIC CONSTRAINTS

Morphologic constraints exert their influence upon the organization of our movements through the structural, functional, perceptual, and organismic variability of the organism. The evolutionary history of human beings, the genetic background of the individual, and the special growth and developmental progress of each individual contribute significantly to this variability. As we look down the animal phylogenetic scale we see that there is a similarity in structural design—the basic skeletal structure—coupled with a "divergence of function" (Lorenz, 1969). "Each species inherits a basic design that will be modified by its mode of maintaining life" (Cooper and Glassow, 1976). Within a species we find that there is also an obvious similarity in structure. In humans, for example, we can talk about the bones, muscles, and connective tissue and the gross similarities of each. We can also talk about similarities in function. The similarities are gross, or average, and thus individual performers must compensate for their own unique morphologic make-up.

These differences in morphology are reflected in the nature of the movement and in the resultant pattern of movement. The student should have clearly in mind that any movement is the result of muscle groups working together ("aggregate muscle action") in order to produce articular action (Logan and McKinney, 1970). The morphologic constraints, therefore, are overcome by organized and coordinated aggregate muscular action. Acting in a sequentially organized fashion, muscle groups perform two major functions:

1. They act as producers of force in a lever system in order to achieve angular or rotary motion at a joint. Angular or rotary motion is then translated into some form of linear movement.
2. They act as stabilizers, an active support system for maintaining the body against the forces of gravity while either stationary or moving.

Structural-functional relationship and morphologic constraints

By structural morphologic constraints we refer to such factors as the structure, design, and composition of the skeletal system (bones) and the structure, design, and composition of the muscles, tendons, and ligaments. These "structures" give the human body its form and provide the mechanism for production of movement. Each of these structural morphologic characteristics is discussed in relation to functional implications.

Structure, design, and composition of skeletal system

The skeletal system has five primary functions:

1. It constitutes a *lever system* to which muscles are attached, thus making movement possible. This is the most important function in relation to our analysis of human movement.
2. It provides a *framework for the support* of the soft structures of the body and thus gives the basic shape to the body. The articular surfaces provide the flexibility or movement within a segmentally linked system.
3. It provides *protection* and *support* for the internal organs and structures.
4. It is a *factory* for the manufacture of red and white blood cells and bone cells.
5. It is a *storehouse* for the manufacture of minerals, salts, and calcium and phosphate.

The skeletal system is made up of two parts: the *axial skeleton*, consisting of the *skull* and the *trunk*, and the *appendicular skeleton*, consisting of the upper limb extremities (arms), the lower limb extremities (legs), and part of the pelvic girdle.

Within the axial skeletal system the trunk is subdivided into the *thorax*, consisting of the ribs and sternum, and the *vertebral column*, consisting of 33 vertebra. The vertebral column is subdivided into four regions: cervical, thoracic, lumbar, and sacralcoccygeal.

Within the appendicular skeleton there are seven subdivisions associated with the upper limbs and consisting of a total of 64 bones, all occurring in pairs: shoulder girdle—clavical and scapula; upper arm—humerus; forearm—radius and ulna; wrist—carpols; hand—metacarpals; fingers—phalanges; and thumb. For the lower limbs there are eight subdivisions consisting of 62 bones: pelvic girdle—illium, ishium, and pubis (fused by adulthood); thigh—femur; knee cap—patella; lower leg—tibia and fibula; ankle—talus and tibial and fibular malleolus; foot—tarsals and metatarsals; toes—phalanges; and big toe.

The bones of the human body are composed of two types of osseous tissue, a solid, *compact* type and a spongy *cancellous* type. In the long bones of the body (majority of the bones of the appendicular skeleton), the shaft portion (middle or diaphysis) consists primarily of a cylinder of compact bone surrounding a central cavity containing the marrow; the ends of the long bones *(epiphyses)* consist largely of cancellous bone covered by a thin layer of compact bone. Compact bone forms a structure providing strength, and its tubular arrangement makes it resistant to bending. The cancellous tissue found at the ends of the long bone gives the bone strength by distributing the impact and action forces over a network of interconnected structures; in addition it reduces the weight of the bone (this is probably due to the increased bone size resulting from a need for a broader articular surface).

The student should realize that bone growth and deterioration is a function of the duration and degree of stress placed upon the bone. We know also that heredity, endocrine function, and nutrition are important factors in bone growth (Rasch and Burke, 1974; Steindler, 1955).

The meeting of two or more bones of the skeleton is called an *articulation,* or *joint*. The articular surfaces and the corresponding arrangement of muscle attachments across these surfaces allow the human system to move. (See Chapter Three for the discussion of degrees of freedom of movement and the kinematic chain of movement.) Each articulation of the body can be classified according to the amount of movement possible: immovable—synarthrodial articulation; slightly movable—amphiarthrodial)[1]; and movable—diarthrodial. Most studies of human move-

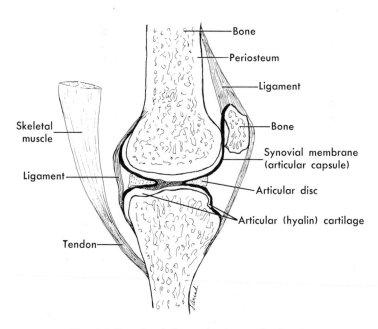

Fig. 8-1. Diarthrodial joint (with articular discs).

Table 4. Diarthrodial articulations

Name	Common name—example of location	Defined	Motions possible
Enarthrodial	Ball and socket joint—hip, shoulder joints	Rounded head of one bone is received into concave surface area of adjoining bone	Have greatest number of degrees of freedom of movement—movement possible through all three anatomic planes
Condyloid	Knee and wrist joints	One or two oval convex surfaces on one bone are received into oval concave surface of adjoining bone—a biaxial articulation	Have two degrees of freedom of movement through two planes; for the knee joint, at full extension there is slight rotation of tibia on femur, called locking-in the knee
Ginglymus	Hinge joint—elbow joint; interphalangeal joint	Articular surfaces concave and convex so motion occurs in one plane only—a uniaxial articulation	Have one degree of freedom of motion—both flexion and extension in sagittal plane only
Trochoid	Pivot joint—radioulnar joint	Pivotlike process turns in ring	Rotation is only movement permitted—permits rotation around vertical axis as in radioulnar joint (as in forearm supination and pronation)
Arthrodial	Gliding joint—wrist, ankle, vertebra	Two or more flat surfaces butting against each other	Usually see movement in terms of sum of series of small movements—movement is dependent upon area in which articulation exists; between any two bones there is little motion
Reciprocal receptor	Saddle joint—carpal and metacarpal joint of thumb (only one in body)	Opposing surfaces are reciprocally concave and convex	Extreme freedom of motion possible—usually thought to be biaxial and thus with two degrees of freedom of motion; however, circumduction is possible and hence some anatomists class as triaxial.

ment are concerned with the *diarthrodial*, or freely movable, articulation. Our discussion of structure and function of the articulations will be limited to the diarthrodial class because of its importance in motor skill and related movement analysis.

Diarthrodial articulations are classified according to bone arrangement. This arrangement determines the type of motion possible at that joint. Diarthrodial articulations have synovial cavities whose function is to cover the joint cavity with fluid for the purpose of lubricating and nourishing the articular cartilage and surrounding tissue (Fig. 8-1). Table 4 lists the diarthrodial articulations and their corresponding functions. The shape of each joint, determined by its structural characteristics, is the primary determinant of the articular function (Steindler, 1955).

Closely associated with the articular structure is the articular cartilage and the ligaments. Articular cartilage is a firm, smooth, highly elastic tissue located on the articular surfaces of bones associated with diarthrodial articulations. Its primary function is to provide a smooth surface against which the bones can move throughout their range of motion. Articular cartilage also functions as a shock absorber, as for example in the intervertebral discs of the spine and in the lateral and medial menisci of the knee joint. *Ligaments* are connective tissue composed of bundles of collagenous fibers in parallel and interlaced with each other. Ligaments pass across, around, or alongside articulations connecting adjacent bones. In the knee joint the cruciate ligaments actually pass between the articulating surfaces. Ligaments are flexible and afford freedom of movement and at the same time reinforce the strength of the articulation by holding the bones together.

The morphologic constraints imposed by the skeletal system relate to the length, size, and shape of our bones and to the structural characteristics of articular surfaces and ligaments. It is, after all, one bone moving against another bone that allows us to place a limb in a particular position at a particular velocity and force. The range of motion at a joint, the amount and type of movement possible, is limited by articular construction as well as by ligament attachment and involvement.

By way of example, we can describe a very interesting phenomenon illustrating one kind of skeletal morphologic constraint that must be overcome in performing many types of movements involving the shoulder girdle, shoulder joint, and the arm. This is what MacConaill and Basmajian (1969:38) call the "swing experiment":

> Let your upper limb hang vertically downwards, the forearm being in semi-pronation, so that the palm is against the lateral side of the thigh. *Keep the forearm semi-pronated during all that follows,* as if the limb were splinted. Now swing the arm directly forwards and upwards (forward flexion) through 90°, so that it is in a horizontal

plane. Next swing backwards (horizontal extension) through 90°. Lastly, adduct it until it is again hanging down (pendant). Observe that the palm is now facing forwards, that is, *the arm has been rotated through 90° at the shoulder joint.* The forearm is, however, still semi-pronated. Now carry out another 90° of forward flexion, another 90° of horizontal flexion and another 90° of full adduction. Note that the dorsum, not the palm, of the hand is now against the thigh, that is, *the arm has now been rotated laterally through a further 90°.* It will be found impossible to repeat the cycle of movements any further until the arm has been medially rotated at the shoulder through 180°, a fact in accordance with the rule that no bone can be rotated through more than two right angles at any joint.

One question raised by this experiment is why the hand by the end of the ergonomic cycle changes position from palm against the body to palm forward. The answer lies in the fact that the movement within the shoulder joint is essentially a three-dimensional movement, whereby a single point on a convex surface is moving against a concave surface. This presents us with a problem in solid geometry whereby the total movement of a single point within the joint travels a distance described by a spherical triangle having the sum of its interior angles greater than 180 degrees. (For a mathematical proof of this phenomenon, the reader should refer to MacConaill and Basmajian's treatment.)

The important point, however, is that for complex movements involving more than one limb segment, the control system must contend with the articular constraints resulting from the construction of each joint involved in the movement. With specific reference to the use of the hands, the constraints imposed by the operation of the shoulder girdle are enormously complicated. They need to be overcome prior to successful completion of any task; for example, to get the hand from some beginning position to an object and return. The articular complexities juxtaposed with the varied size and shape of the bones themselves should be appreciated by students concerned with the organization of movement. Each of us can choose a variety of ways to motorically solve the swing experiment. This particular constraint has to be overcome in movements involving the shoulder, arm, and hand, such as the tennis serve, throwing, and batting. How each performer solves this constraint will produce a unique pattern of movement for that task. This is just one of an infinite variety of problems posed by morphologic constraints.

Injury to ligaments, bones, and muscles can change the morphologic structure sufficiently to necessitate reorganization of the movement. In part this may be why for certain types of injuries athletes feel they have partially to relearn a task or skill. They are reorganizing, replanning, and reshaping their motor plans to deal with the new imposed morphologic constraint. The morphologic constraints as they relate to the skeletal system are only part of the picture. We must now consider the contractile elements that produce the movement of the rigid links in the skeletal system.

Structure, design, and composition of muscular system

The muscular system of the body provides the forces by which we are able to move. The skeletal muscles always cross one or more articulations and attach themselves to our bones via tendonous tissue (Fig. 8-1). The attachment of muscles to the skeletal structure of the body is always achieved in such a manner that movement of the body segments occurs at the articulations. The muscles of our body, therefore, produce the forces that move a lever system consisting of links of bone.

A muscle can only *contract* or *relax*. *Muscles do not push,* as many beginning students tend to believe. Any pushing, pulling, or rotating effect achieved by our limbs or body is the direct result of the interplay between contracting and relaxing muscles acting across an articulation or series of articulations. Contraction of a muscle shortens the muscle, which produces movement at a joint or series of joints, provided there is no counterforce from an opposing muscle or from an external source, as in isometric or lengthening contraction. Muscular contraction acts upon the movable links of the skeletal system to produce a specified movement.

As was pointed out in Chapter Five, the voluntary contraction of skeletal muscle is a function of the sensory and motor properties of the system at any moment in time. The normal voluntary function of muscular contraction producing the movement is dependent upon the constant interplay between sensory information derived from the muscles, tendons, and joints and the effector influences on the contracting musculature. The muscle spindles, located in the intrafusal muscle fibers, and their associated gamma efferent system of motor control provide one form of feedback control directly related to the length of the muscle and the rate of change of muscle length. The Golgi tendon bodies provide information about muscle tension, and the joint receptors provide information about joint displacement or angular movement at a joint. The ultimate movement outcome is thus the result of the interplay of efferent control against the background of sensory information and control. A basic knowledge of the structure and function of muscle will enhance our understanding and appreciation of this complex system of control.

The morphologic constraints imposed by the structure of the muscle are related to three factors: the sensory-motor control properties (discussed in Chapter Five), the general anatomic structure of the muscles and their related function, and the anatomic design of muscle placement on the bones and across their respective articulations. The structure and placement of skeletal muscles determine their function.

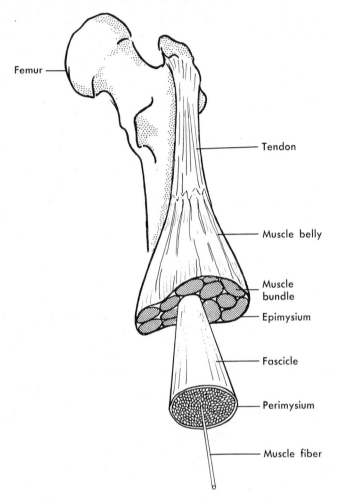

Femur

Tendon

Muscle belly

Muscle bundle

Epimysium

Fascicle

Perimysium

Muscle fiber

Fig. 8-2. Muscle and tendon attachment to bone and related arrangement of muscular tissue.

Tendons are a form of connective tissue called fasciae and provide the terminal attachments for muscle to connect to the bone. Fascia is fibrous material of heavy collagenous bundles held together by rather delicate cross-fibers. (The tendon is usually a narrow band or cord attached to the bone.) Fasciae hold bundles of muscle fibers together and are continuous with the tendon. This type of construction determines the direction of force for each contracting muscle (Fig. 8-2).

Muscle physiologists and kinesiologists have identified two basic

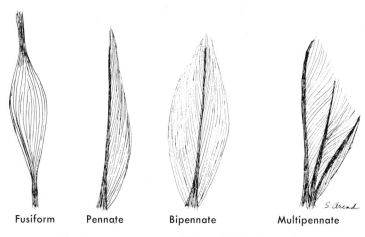

Fusiform   Pennate   Bipennate   Multipennate

Fig. 8-3. Arrangement of fibers of skeletal muscles.

skeletal muscle structures: fusiform and pennate (Fig. 8-3). The *fusiform* muscle structure distributes the muscle fibers in a longitudinal fashion along the tendon. The *pennate* muscle structure distributes the muscle fibers in a diagonal fashion along one side of the tendon (as the plumes of a feather). A *bipennate* muscle has diagonal fibers converging on the tendon from both sides (e.g., rectus femoris muscle) and a *multipennate* muscle has diagonal fibers converging on several tendons (e.g., deltoid muscle). This muscle structure has a direct relationship to the force a muscle can develop. Muscles of the fusiform type, having their fibers arranged in parallel to the tendon, have a greater range of motion for contraction but cannot generate as much force as the pennate type muscle. Muscles of the pennate type, with diagonally arranged muscle fibers, can generate greater force and initial speed of movement but sacrifice range of motion.

For any given movement the force a muscle can generate and the range of motion through which it contracts is directly related to the structure of the muscle. The three structural factors most directly related to the generation of muscular force are the internal arrangement of the muscle fibers, the number of muscle fibers per cross-sectional area of the muscle, and the girth of the muscle. These factors are obviously different for each individual and may for many reasons vary over time for any individual. In addition, slight variation in attachment from individual to individual will alter the action of the lever system provided by the skeletal system. Thus we can see that the skeletal muscle structure in conjunction with the skeletal system is an important morphologic constraint.

Consideration of morphologic constraints as a function of the nature and type of muscular attachment needs some explanation. Attachments of muscles across the joints of our body results in a force-lever system. The muscles provide the necessary force and direction of force as a function of their structure and anatomic placement. Muscle contraction brings about a shortening in both directions of the muscle; that is, the force generated by a contracting muscle is the same at each attachment. In addition, the contractile forces are attempting to bring both attachments together. In most movements one link is usually more stationary than the adjacent link. Which link is stationary and which is movable is dependent upon the desired movement. The desired movement is brought about by the interplay between oposing muscle groups. Our muscles work in groups and not as single muscles (though often for clarity we refer to action of a single muscle).

For any articulation a muscle or group of muscles essentially acts on each side of the joint. This is referred to as the nature of the muscle attachment. These opposing muscles work together to produce the desired control and force modulation for any particular movement. The muscle group producing the movement is called the *"muscle most involved,"* a descriptive term to indicate location during active movement.[2] With respect to the joint, the muscle pull is "parallel to or within the plane of motion through which" the segment moves (Logan and McKinney, 1970:67). The muscle group located on the opposite side of the articulation from the muscles most involved is called the *contralateral muscle group*. Contralateral muscles function along with the muscles most involved to produce the desired movement. Also working with the muscles most involved and the contralateral muscles are guiding and stabilizing muscles. *Guiding muscles* help to rule out undesired actions of other participating muscle groups. *Stabilizing muscles* aid in holding the limb segments in a position against which adjacent segments can move.

The actual type of attachment of a muscle—where each end of a muscle or group of muscles attach in relation to joint and bone—is another important morphologic consideration. This is a problem of lever action. The attachment of a muscle across the articulation to a specific point on the adjacent segments will determine the distance and direction of forces applied to the lever arm. If a muscle is to act as a power or spurt muscle its proximal attachment[3] is usually a relatively greater distance away from the articular center of motion, and the distal attachment is near the articular center of motion, thus increasing the effective length of the force arm. Mechanically this produces a force across the articulation rather than along the axis of the moving segment. In most movements the proximal segment is stabilized in relation to the distal segments; for example, when we throw a ball, the trunk initiates the movement, then provides a base of support for continued action of subsequent and adjacent limb action. The upper arm thus acts upon the stabilized trunk and itself successively stabilizes for the lower arm action—summation of internal forces.

If a muscle is to act as a speed or shunt muscle its proximal attachment will usually be relatively closer to the articular center of motion, and the distal attachment is a greater distance from the articular center of motion, thus increasing the resistance arm. Mechanically this produces a muscular action primarily along the long axis of the moving segment; the pull is toward the articulation.

PERCEPTUAL PROCESSES AND ORGANISMIC VARIABLES AS MORPHOLOGIC CONSTRAINTS

Perceptual processes and organismic variables are included as morphologic constraints because their effect upon the organization of the movement is directly related to specific structures and forms of the organism. Perceptual processes relate to sensory and motor structures and functions: sensory detection, encoding, memory, translation, and motor output. Organismic variables are related to the final form of the interdependent parts and subordinate elements comprising the organism as a whole: sex, size, shape, age, and so on. In skilled movements perceptual processes in large part function to match not only environmental conditions but also organismic variables such as size, shape, age, sex, and experience. The interrelationship is functionally a match between information detection, information processing, motor response, and the form or structure of the organism.

In terms of perceptual variables, only a very general statement seems appropriate for this text. "The perceptual processes required for performance of a skill depend upon the environmental conditions under which the skill is carried out" (Spaeth, 1972:338). These environmental conditions have been discussed in Chapter Six. A major perceptual variable the performer must overcome in order to succeed when performing or acquiring motor skill is the time lags inherent in the system.

Time lags refer to elapsed time between a stimulus and the first detectable response; the time required to detect and process information from the environment and to respond by initiating a muscular response, thus putting into motion the appropriate limb segments and the body. For example, the youngster learning to hit a baseball finds difficulty in being coincident with it. In part this is due to the inability to predict and anticipate the flight characteristics of the ball in time and space and in turn to position the body and limbs so the appropriate movements can be made. As a performer makes environmental predictions and anticipates where an object will be in space and time, the movements are projected into the future, thus overcoming the time lags inherent in the system and allowing the movement to be coincident with the event.

Time lags are the sum of information processing and effector response time (motoneuron transmission time, muscle contraction time, and force generation time required for moving the limbs in the appropriate direction at the appropriate velocity and time). The time lag is thus the system time required to receive internal and external environmental information, process this information, predict the spatial and temporal characteristics of the object and thus anticipate where it will be at some future point in time, and generate a motor response that will be coincident with it. Experience and practice aid the learner in overcoming these time lags.

Organismic variables such as body and limb size (height, weight, and limb length), sex, and age impose several important constraints upon the overall organization of movement. Though at present we can only speculate from personal experience and deduce from a smattering of seemingly unrelated empirical evidence, it does seem reasonable to assume that patterns of movement are directly related to these organismic variables. For a specific skill, the outlined organismic variables will have direct impact upon the manner in which the performer realizes successful goal achievement and will hence be reflected in the pattern of movement.

Body size and limb segment length relate to differences in body and limb mass and to the nature and placement of muscular attachments. Motorically overcoming the variability in segmental and total body mass, in addition to overall height and length of segments, is a perceptual process of motor control. The student and teacher must understand that this is unique for each individual and therefore each performer's pattern of movement for a specific task or skill will be unique.

Sex differences also provide an additional morphologic variable. It is known, for example, that the general structural construction of the female pelvic girdle and that fat distribution in the female are different from those of the male. These two factors, among others, tend to lower the center of gravity of the female performer. The morphologic difference related to size of pelvic girdle will obviously reflect itself in two general ways: pattern of movement and manner in which muscular forces can effectively be applied.

Age is also considered a morphologic constraint because growth and development of the structure and related changes occurring in the organization of the movement affect the pattern of movement. As children grow their bones and related musculature also grow. In order to cope with the motoric demands of the environment the growing organism must continually adjust for the changes in the morphology. As stated earlier, the process of aging also has a morphologic effect—loss of range of motion, flexibility, strength, and endurance—and hence affects the organization of movement.

Serious consideration needs to be given to how these organismic variables affect the learning of a motor skill. Each performer arrives on the learning scene with different capacities and unique morphologic structure and form. We should therefore not expect the performer to match some ideal form. Attention must be given to structuring the learning environment, directing instruction, and providing meaningful practice given our understanding of the effect of perceptual processes and organismic variables upon movement organization. This attention and consideration should encompass all that can be synthesized about the effect of morphologic constraints on movement.

COMPENSATING FOR MORPHOLOGIC CONSTRAINTS

For a specific task or skill, the performer and the teacher have at their disposal several ways in which they can compensate for morphologic constraints: (1) develop a pattern of movement commensurate with the uniqueness of the performer's morphology, (2) select skills in which the performance requirements appear more or less to match the morphology of the performer, (3) change the strategy employed in a game or task, (4) change the rules of the activity, and (5) appropriately design equipment and performance environments. None of these five points is mutually exclusive, nor are they by any means definitive or absolute.

The uniqueness of movements to a considerable extent will be a function of the organism's morphology. This uniqueness, as we have seen, is reflected in different patterns of movement for each performer for each task or skill. Recent work by Gentile et al. (1975) has, however, posed a slight modification to this statement. While it is true that for any task the pattern of movement is different for each performer, it does appear that within certain limits some of the abstract parameters of the movement look very similar from performer to performer. This finding suggests that the environment has a pervasive influence upon the ultimate organization of the movement and that any differences in the pattern of movement between performers may be the result of different morphologic make-up. The environment should be viewed as an important interacting constraint. Both the teacher's and the student's approach to a skill will differ, depending upon the performer's morphology. For the individual performer, muscle strength, size, height, weight, segmental length, and receptor function (for example, visual receptors) determine the most effective and efficient way to produce a movement. The environmental and biomechanical factors set the invariant properties to which the performer's movements must be matched.

There is some evidence that performers select specific types of skilled activity on the basis of morphologic constraints. Though open to criticism, this notion is made more tenable when we include perceptual processes and organismic variables as morphologic constraints. Recognition of other factors, however, is also important—interest, personality, and experience. For example, it may well be that on the basis of size and strength many performers select themselves out of certain types of contact sports. Visual receptor function may also play a role in the self-selection for a particular type of activity. Activities such as tennis and baseball may have performance elements that demand a visual receptor system able to operate at a very discriminatory level. In some sports, skills, and dance, where aesthetics is an important factor, discrimination or selection of performers may also be made on the basis of morphology. The discrimination may be on the basis of the nature of activity or for purely aesthetic reasons.

Changing strategy and rules are to some degree related to morphologic constraints. Though there are others, the primary morphologic constraint affecting this compensatory factor is *age*. Age is related to morphologic growth, development, and decline. Rules in many sports activities are changed to compensate for age differences, differing growth rates and sizes, and, of course, experience. As one approaches the years of morphologic decline, strategy compensates for limits in strength, endurance, and flexibility. In addition, the performer may select entirely different types of activities as the years of morphologic decline begin to approach.

Though originally listed as environmental constraints, the design of equipment and performance environments is an important *morphologic compensating factor*. The size, weight, and shape of implements (balls, bats, rackets, protective gear) are designed to conform to the morphology of the performer. For the young basketball player, the basket is often set lower, as is the net in games such as volleyball and badminton. Equipment is also designed to improve performance, for example, the javelin, vaulting pole, diving boards, and so on. It is interesting to note that change in equipment design also has an effect upon the ultime technique employed and the morphologic type of performer. For example, with the advent of the fiberglass pole, pole vaulters have changed their technique, and the perfomers seem to be of a different morphologic structure than they were when the stiffer bamboo and metal poles were used.

The uniqueness of the pattern of movement for a particular performer for a specific task is a function of morphologic constraints. Organized human movement entails compensating for these constraints. An interesting story recently related to me will serve as a summary statement for this chapter. The essential point is how a teacher and a student were able to work out ways of compensating for a rather gross morphologic divergence.

In a beginning college course in skiing, one of the students had a great deal of difficulty keeping balanced while either standing or moving down the hill. He was constantly tripping over himself, catching his edges when attempting to shift position or to turn, and he was generally finding himself completely frustrated and discouraged. Upon careful study, the instructor realized that this student had extremely bowed legs. She immediately realized that his inability to stand on the ski slope, to ski, and to turn was a direct function of his bowed legs. As should be obvious to those who have skied at all, he could not keep the bottoms of his skis flat on the skiing surface, nor could he properly control his edges. The most critical element in movement at this level of skill was control of edges; as the skier turns he must be able to control the ski edges so that the skis move in unison or in parallel, so control of speed and direction are effective.

Once the problem was recognized, the solution quickly became apparent. Lifters would have to be built into his boots (the outside edge of the sole of his ski boots would have to be raised). This would serve to change the angle of the ski with the skiing surface, while not altering the morphology. Lifters would compensate for a morphologic constraint. This seemed to help to some extent, though not quite enough. The instructor then realized that in addition to an equipment design change, the skiing technique would have to change for this particular student. It was then suggested to the student that he should attempt to ski with his skis slightly apart and with a little more bend in his knees than is usually suggested. His resultant pattern of movement was different, and some of the techniques for turning had to be adjusted. However, to bring the story to a happy ending, the student began to enjoy his skiing for the first time and found that he could successfully traverse, turn, and schuss down the hill.

NOTES

1. *Synarthrodial articulations* are also called fibrous articulations. They have no synovial cavities and thus are immovable. Sutures (or junctions) such as those between the bones of the skull are the prime example of this class. *Amphiarthrodial articulations* are slightly movable and include two subclasses: *symphyses*—immovable, or more or less immovable, such as pubic symphyses; and *syndesmoses*—contiguous surfaces of the bones are rough and are bound together by an interosseous ligament or membrane, such as between the radius and ulna.

2. Logan and McKinney (1970) have suggested a new terminology for describing the action of muscles based upon location during a specific movement. "*Muscle most involved*" replaces the terms "agonist," "prime mover," and "assistant

mover"; *"contralateral muscles"* replaces the term "antagonist"; *"guiding muscles"* replaces the terms "synergy" and "helping synergy"; and *"stabilizing muscles"* replaces the term "fixation."

3. *Proximal attachment* of a muscle: the attachment to the bone is closer to the midline of the body. *Distal attachment* of a muscle: the attachment of the bone is away from the midline of the body.

NINE

Tools of analysis

We come now to a central aspect of our quest for understanding the nature of human movement and its relationship to the acquisition of skilled motor performance. How can we analyze human movement? What approaches seem appropriate, given the level of analysis selected? As suggested in Chapter Four, a theoretical base for the understanding of human movement involves consideration of levels of analysis and the environmental, biomechanical, and morphologic constraints with which the learner or performer must contend. Each of these has been reviewed in the preceding chapters, and the task now at hand is to explore the variety of approaches available to the student, the teacher, and the researcher for analyzing movement, be it a complex or simple task or skill, a discrete movement, an advanced or a beginning performer.

Regardless of our individual perspective, in the quest for information and knowledge about human movement at some point we must be able to analyze in a systematic fashion the movements that produce some form of environmental outcome—goal-directed movement. Students learning new skills want to understand how they are moving relative to the goals of the skills. The ability to analyze and evaluate one's own performance may facilitate the acquisition of skill. The teacher can play a central role in this situation. This role is fourfold: self-analysis and evaluation of movement, analysis and evaluation of individual performance, analysis and understanding of the nature of a particular skill, and understanding of performance-related feedback appropriate to the skill. To a degree this also encompasses several basic notions related to facilitation of skill acquisition, more broadly explored in Chapter Ten.

Two broad approaches can be identified for the study, analysis, and evaluation of goal-directed movements: qualitative and quantitative methods. The broad category selected depends upon the nature of the questions asked, the purposes of the analysis, and the information desired. The intent of this chapter, therefore, is to explore for each category the most appropriate methods of analysis of human movement.

It is useful to distinguish between analysis of skill and analysis of performance. When we analyze a skill our considerations are broader and related more to a description of a specific skill, like the forehand drive in tennis or a forward sommersault in gymnastics or diving, without reference to individual performer differences and levels of skill acquisition. When we analyze performance, we consider the individual performer on a specific task. Analysis of skill is largely a descriptive model, while analysis of performance relates specifically to the individual performing.

Qualitative methods or tools of analysis are largely observational. They involve descriptive techniques that provide the student, teacher, or researcher with a means of systematically determining the nature or distinguishing characteristics of a movement through direct observation. *Quantitative methods* or tools of analysis are largely measurement oriented. They employ tools and techniques involving measurement in order to determine the amount or proportions of the structural elements of the movement. If, for example, we were interested in the performance of a child throwing a baseball, a qualitative approach would involve a systematic description of that performance based upon our guided observation. A quantitative approach would involve utilization of tools that measure the various parameters of the movement: displacement, velocity, acceleration, muscular contraction, and the like. A descriptive value is placed on one and a numerical (or even probabilistic or statistical) value on the other.

In either case, the type of analysis chosen must fit the needs of the user. The point common to both categories is that they are systematic. Systematic observation or measurement increases our chance of knowing what we are looking for in the movement; we understand what the essential elements of the skill or task are and what they might mean. Whether the interest is in observation or measurement of movements, or both, the analytic method employed serves as a plan of observation that is systematic and related to the type of information required.

An in-depth treatment of descriptive and observational tools for analysis is often neglected by teachers and researchers in motor skill. Hopefully some of the material presented in this area will provide a firm theoretical and systematic basis for observation of movement. Quantitative methods are discussed here only to the extent that they enhance and extend our ability to observe. Readers interested in a more in-depth treatment of this area are referred to Miller and Nelson (1973).

QUALITATIVE TOOLS OF ANALYSIS

Qualitative analysis is generally observational, descriptive, and for the observer, usually subjective. However, when a theoretically sound and simply constructed systematic system for observing and describing movement is used in conjunction with one's experience and knowledge about a particular skill, the subjectivity of the tool can be minimized.

The observation and description of movement is a valuable and useful tool for the following reasons:

1. It focuses attention upon the sequence of movement events.
2. It identifies and therefore directs our attention to the most significant aspects of a particular skill or movement sequence.
3. It systematizes thinking related to the relationship between the movement and the outcome.
4. It identifies those elements of the movement that are useful in instruction and performance feedback.
5. It aids in evaluating the development of a particular skill and assessing performance over time.

For the teacher, qualitative analysis helps to see the movement. Coaches are often very proficient at observing movement; they are often very systematic and exceptionally well versed in the technique of their particular sport interest. It would be well for more teachers and researchers in human movement to develop similar astute sensitivity when observing skill and performance.

Several types of tools are readily identified that can aid qualitative analysis. Regardless of the tool selected, trained systematic observation is the key to reliable and objective analysis. We use our eyes to observe the actual performance or we observe performance recorded cinematographically, on videotape, as sequences of still photographs (graph check camera), or on photographs, drawings, and loop films. Various systems of qualitative analysis of motor skill and performance have been proposed and extensively used by teachers and researchers studying human movement. These are often cumbersome and limited in scope and information, since they are related to specific situations or skills.

The types of analysis proposed by a number of writers might be typified as follows: segmental analysis (Logan and McKinney, 1970); anatomic analysis (Wells, 1971); skill/performance description (Rasch and Burke, 1974); direct subjective analysis (Arend and Higgins, 1976).

Though there are several features within these forms of analysis that are similar, it will be useful to briefly outline each.

Segmental analysis

Logan and McKinney (1970) have suggested a useful observational form of analysis that essentially views the body in segments, the major

moving parts of the body, and as a totality in the "total performance" of
the task. The following is a listing of major headings and salient points for
consideration adapted from Logan and McKinney (1970):

1. *Total performance or "whole movement":* consider such features as
   overall coordination, timing of the movement, summation of
   forces, and performance outcome.
2. *Base of support:* consider foot placement, shifts in support, and
   projection of base of support.
3. *Pelvic area and rib cage:* consider the direction, rotation, extent,
   and forces involved in moving the pelvic region; with respect to
   the rib cage observe the movement in relation to the pelvic area.
   Included here might also be the position, directions, and extent of
   theoretical center of gravity of the body.
4. *Shoulder area:* consider the movement of the shoulder girdle, timing of movement, and forces involved.
5. *Head:* consider head positions in relation to proper orientation of
   the head to place visual system in more advantageous position for
   monitoring and gathering environmental information.
6. *Arms and hands:* consider directions of movement, type of limb
   manipulation involved, the range of movement, implements used,
   rotation, and bilaterality of movement (use of arms and hands in
   opposition or together).
7. *Hips and knees:* consider direction of movement, actions of hip and
   knee throughout the movement, rotation at the pelvis, relationship
   of pelvic movement in relation to trunk, arms, and legs.
8. *Follow-through:* consider the extent and direction of the pattern of
   movement, segments involved in breaking the movement, length
   of follow-through, position of body and base of support in relation
   to any subsequent performance.
9. *Total performance reviewed:* consider effectiveness of the movement, of summation of internal forces, and degree of goal accomplishment.

Fig. 9-1 presents an adapted worksheet for this form of analysis. Note
that in addition to a breakdown of body segments, the phases of the
skill or movement (ergonomic cycle)—preparatory, action, and follow-
through—are also included.

Readers are also referred to Roebuck (1968) who proposes a "mobility
model" for describing movement of body segments. This system has been
developed for determining man-machine relationships in the space program and incorporates several useful human engineering principles.

Anatomic analysis

As outlined in Chapter Two, analysis from an anatomic point of view
considers the function of individual muscles or groups of muscles in rela-

Segments observed	Preparatory phase	Action phase	Follow-through phase
1. Total performance			
2. Base of support			
3. Pelvic area and rib cage			
4. Shoulder			
5. Head			
6. Arms and hands			
7. Hip and knees			
8. The follow-through			
9. Total performance reviewed			

Worksheet to be used for analysis of skill or analysis of individual performance. Prior to analyzing performance, some notation of expected observations with respect to the skill should be made in each cell. During repeated observations of single performances the observer can check-off whether or not the expected movement outcome occurred. Any additional and pertinent observations should also be noted in each cell of the worksheet.

Fig. 9-1. Segmental analysis worksheet.

Movement or skill analyzed _____   (Complete for each phase of movement-preparatory action and follow-through phases.)

Name of joint(s)	Action of joint	Muscles active	Type of muscle contraction	Type of body movement	Type and amount of contraction	General comments
Cervical spine						
Thoracic and lumbar spine						
Pelvic girdle						
Hip joint						
Knee joint						
Ankle joint and foot						
Shoulder girdle						
Shoulder joint						
Elbow and radial/ulnar joints						

Fig. 9-2. Anatomic analysis worksheet. (Modified from Rasch and Burke, 1974.)

tion to described actions at each joint participating in a given movement. Though this system is cumbersome and of limited value for most observational situations, it does have merit in several situations. The most obvious value is in prescriptive exercise and in exercises or skills where development of strength, endurance, and flexibility are important concomitants. The teacher may wish to develop an exercise regime for achieving strength, endurance, or flexibility at a specific point in the range of movement for a particular skill. When the actions of individual muscles or muscle groups in relation to a particular movement are understood, this process is enhanced.

The most satisfactory treatments of anatomic analysis can be found in Rasch and Burke (1974) and Wells (1971). Fig. 9-2 depicts a worksheet that incorporates the classification system described in Chapter Two (kinesiologic joint actions) and corresponding muscle actions. This worksheet is by necessity a simplified and shortened version, and it is presented for illustrative purposes.

Descriptive analysis of skill and performance

In some respects descriptive analysis is similar to segmental analysis. However, descriptive analysis focuses primarily on the action occurring at each joint, while segmental analysis focuses upon limb displacement. Descriptive analysis is worthwhile in that it illuminates several interesting points and elements important in describing a skill or an individual performance. The following nine points, adapted from Rasch and Burke (1974), should be taken into account when describing movement:

1. *Posture and body position throughout the movement:* described in relation to preparatory, action, and follow-through phases.
2. *Direction of action at each joint:* described in terms of joint movements defined for anatomic classification (flexion, extension, abduction, adduction, etc.).
3. *Type of motion at each joint:* described in terms of fixation, dynamic and ballistic movement (see Hartson, 1939).
4. *Sequence of joint actions:* described in terms of phases of movement and sequential relationship of participating joints.
5. *Speed and acceleration of joint actions:* described in terms of summation of internal forces and relationship of acceleratory action and achievement and maintenance of speed of movement.
6. *Force of joint actions:* described in terms of description of those joints or limb segments producing maximum to minimum force.
7. *Source of "motive" power for each joint action:* described primarily in terms of type of muscular contraction (concentric, eccentric, static, or isotonic, isometric, philometric contraction). The effects of external forces, such as gravity, are also considered here.

8. *Spatial and temporal coordination and rhythmic patterns of joint actions:* described in terms of sequential relationships and integrated patterns of joint actions.
9. *Required muscular, skeletal, or external stabilization, if any:* described in relation to whole movement and individual joints.

Direct subjective analysis

Direct subjective analysis has been developed by Professor Susan Arend and myself and used extensively in undergraduate and graduate courses at Hunter College, CUNY and Teachers College, Columbia University. We believe it includes the best features of each of the above described forms of analysis and has the added feature of incorporating the "composite model for the classification of movements and skill," described in Chapter Two, with the environmental, biomechanical, and morphologic constraints discussed in the three preceding chapters. One of the important points developed in Chapter Four deals with the need to have a movement classification system clearly in mind, a system that is concerned with type of movement and environmental conditions. In addition, such features as goal of the movement, pattern of movement, kinematic and kinetic factors, described constraints, and level of skill are important features of this analytic approach. Fig. 9-3 schematically represents a strategy for subjective analysis and observation of human movement.

A useful, easily applied, systematic qualitative analytic tool will describe first what should happen, then what actually happened, and finally, by comparing expectations with outcomes, will evaluate the performance and describe the feedback appropriate for the subsequent performance. The model depicted in Fig. 9-3 can be used

> on a one time basis (performance) or on an ongoing basis (acquisition) to view tasks involving simple or complex movements, motor skills, and/or parts or phases of simple or complex movements and motor skills. (Arend and Higgins, 1976:37.)

The strategy involves three stages: preobservation, observation, and postobservation. The preobservation stage involves the observer's systematic collection of information "through a multi-level breakdown or decomposition of the movement" (Arend and Higgins, 1976). The first decision is one of classification of the movement. Though we suggest the "composite classification," the method is satisfactory only to the extent that it is understood and meets the needs of the observer. (Broer's [1968] or Cooper and Glassow's [1976] system may be equally satisfactory.) After classifying the skill we identify the goal of the movement or skill in relation to how the performer perceives it. This is the first level of de-

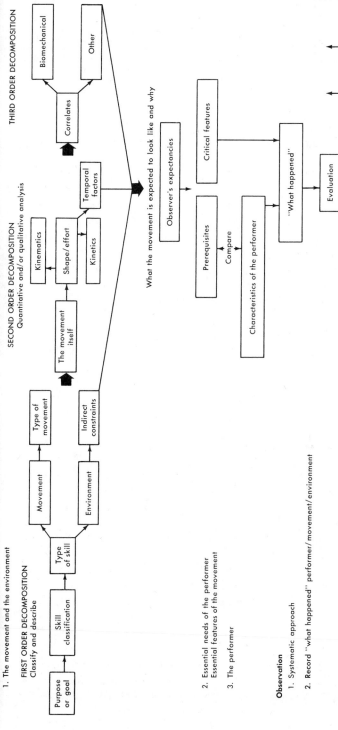

Fig. 9-3. Strategy for subjective analysis and observation of human movement (From Arend, S., and Higgins, J.: *Journal of Human Movement Studies*, 1976, 2, 36-52.)

composition. It is the initial breakdown of the skill into its parts and elements. Consideration is given to factors relating to the general nature of the movement—to support the body, to transport the body, to suspend the body, to impart or receive force, and to achieve speed, accuracy, form, or force in the movement. These considerations are made prior to and following each performance observation.

For the second order of decomposition we suggest a more detailed breakdown of component parts of the movement in terms of phases—preparation, action, and follow-through—and if appropriate, related segmental or joint actions. The spatial and temporal ordering of the movement sequences in relation to important segments or joints is considered. These are the basic kinematic factors—observation of the movement itself without reference to the forces producing it—and we consider segmental displacement, velocity, acceleration, degree of motion, limb-trunk relationships, and body position throughout each phase of the movement. This might then be related to the condition of the environment throughout each phase of the movement. Relationships between environment and body, body transport, and limb manipulation are thus established.

Appropriate biomechanical, kinesiologic and physiologic correlates make up the third order of decomposition of the skill or performance. The objective for this preobservational category is to focus the observer's attention on the mechanics of the movement itself, the kinetic factors involved, and the anatomic and physiologic factors involved. Primary attention is directed toward the biomechanical goals of the movement that relate to movements for production of accuracy, speed, force, and projection and reception of external objects. The principles derived from the three basic biomechanical constructs developed in Chapter Seven—summation of internal forces, aerodynamics, and hydrodynamics—include principles of leverage, laws of motion, maintenance of equilibrium, path and position of body center of gravity, buoyancy, gravity, and centripital and centrifugal forces.

The kinetic factors—the nature and effects of the forces producing the movement—include magnitude, direction, distance, and point of application of force. Kinesiologic correlates relate to quality and efficiency of neuromuscular integration (differential relaxation) necessary for successful goal accomplishment. When applicable, the physiologic correlates relate to the degree of strength, endurance, and flexibility of the performer. This may also include consideration of type of muscular contraction.

The two final preobservational categories deal with skill elements of performance and characteristics of the performer that the observer deems essential for successful goal accomplishment. The observer identifies the elements of the movement that might be essential subgoals for the performance. Later they may become useful instructional variables. By giving attention to elements of performance essential to the performer, first the level of skill is identified, followed by consideration of specific, individual morphologic constraints that may have a relationship to successful goal attainment.

In essence, the preobservation stage of descriptive analysis "represents the synthesis of prerequisite information to teaching itself along with serving the function of setting the stage for meaningful observation and evaluation" (Arend and Higgins, 1976:37).

The primary concern of the observational stage of the analysis is to have clearly in mind what one expects to observe and then note what actually happened. A systematic approach for observation and recording must be selected prior to observing a skill or a performance. It is in this stage that what happened with respect to the performer, the movement, and the environment is recorded. Recording of observations may take one of several forms: noncinematographic observation of total or partial performance, cinematographic or videotape observation, and electromyography or electrogoniometry. Regardless of form, the recording of observation must be systematic and must "provide sufficient information about the performer, movement, and environment to assist the observer in making a meaningful observation" (Arend and Higgins, 1976:46).

The postobservation stage involves a careful comparison of expectation and observation, of what the observer expected to see and what he actually saw. This stage is critical in that it employs evaluative information from the first two stages as useful feedback to the teacher (observer) and the performer. Feedback is provided related to the degree of goal accomplishment, the appropriateness of the movement to the environmental constraints, and the general or specific efficiency of the movement.

For a more detailed discussion of the strategy for observation just described the reader should see Arend and Higgins (1976). Skill in observing movement comes only with practice and a good working system for analysis. The teacher should find this strategy helpful when planning, presenting, and evaluating lessons. The researcher should likewise find the strategy useful as a preliminary step to quantitative analysis, both for sharpening the question to be posed and for getting a feel for the task or skill to be studied.

In order to apply the information contained in Fig. 9-1 a worksheet consisting of a series of questions that incorporate the essential features of the strategy is included in two forms: a complete and detailed worksheet, pp. 130-131, and a greatly reduced or short worksheet, p. 132.

Before moving on to a discussion of the quantitative tools of analysis, it should be pointed out that many of the photographic techniques in use

---

**Worksheet for direct subjective
analysis of motor skill**

I. *Preobservation:* What the observer expects to find. The classification, description, and analysis of the movement to be observed; relate the expected observation to the performer.
  A. How would you classify the movement?
  Discuss:
    1. The goal of the movement.
    2. The role of the environment: the spatial and temporal components and constraints.
    3. The type of movement to be observed.
  B. What is the most general (primary) method of decomposing this skill?
    1. Identify the categories of events or movements; break the movement into its more general parts or phases.
    2. Provide a general description of the movement.
  C. What is the second order of decomposition of the movement?
    1. Describe the movements in each category or phase in terms of the linear and angular kinematics, segmental and/or joint actions, shape considerations.
    2. Describe the movements in each category or phase in terms of the linear and angular kinetics, temporal factors, effort considerations.
  D. What is the third order of decomposition? Identify the appropriate biomechanical, kinesiologic, physiologic, aesthetic, strategic, and morphologic correlates of each phase of the movement.
  E. What parts of the movement are essential for successful performance? Identify:
    1. The critical features of the movement for the observer and the performer to focus upon.
    2. The parts of the movement that the performer can most easily and least easily modify.
II. *Observation:* What is actively occurring during each trial. This should be systematic and involve either a qualitative or quantitative approach. It might include direct observation (cinematographic or noncinematographic) or measurement using displacement, velocity, acceleration, or electromyographic techniques.
  A. Record, systematically, for each observation.

From Arend, S., and Higgins, J. R. A strategy for the classification, subjective analysis, and observation of human movement. *Journal of Human Movement Studies,* 1976, 2, 36–52, 49–50.

B. Be sure to note:
   1. The specific objective of the performer on each trial.
   2. If the performer executed the movement as he planned on each trial.
   3. Any extraneous movements.
   4. The direct environmental influences (spatial and temporal constraints).
   5. The indirect environmental influences (noise, attire, spectators, equipment, etc.).
III. *Postobservation:* Evaluation and feedback considerations made by the observer.
   A. What single aspect of the performance was clearest in your mind during the performance?
      1. Good and bad features of the movement.
      2. Spatial and temporal components of the movement.
      3. Body position, joint and segmental action, etc.
   B. Was the movement coordinated and efficient?
      1. Degree of goal attainment: observer's versus performer's assessment.
      2. Did the performer execute the movement the way he planned?
      3. Extraneous movements.
      4. Differential relaxation: exhibited by smoothness of the movement from phase to phase.
   C. What environmental factors appeared to affect this performance?
      Referring back to the type and condition of the environment, identify:
      1. Appropriateness of the movement and movement strategy to the type and condition of the environment.
      2. Effectiveness of the performer's movement in matching environmental constraints.
      3. Indirect environment influences.
   D. What is the most appropriate feedback to provide to the performer?
      1. Identify and consider feedback related to the movement, outcome of the movement, and skill level of the performer.
      2. List the hierarchical order for the presentation of the feedback.
      3. Consider the appropriate time for providing feedback.

**Abbreviated worksheet for direct subjective
analysis of a motor skill**

Stage:	*Identify:*
Preobservation	1. Goal of the movement
	2. Critical features
Observation	3. Single aspect of performance clearest in your mind
	4. Unnecessary movements and other signs of hypertension
	5. Critical features executed and not executed
Postobservation	6. Degree of goal achievement
	7. Efficiency evaluation
	8. Feedback

From Arend, S., and Higgins, J. R. A strategy for the classification, subjective analysis, and observation of human movement. *Journal of Human Movement Studies*, 1976, 2, 36–52, 51.

today, especially cinematography and videotape, can be excellent permanent records of skill and performance with which to practice and study observational techniques. Finally, videotape provides an excellent means of systematically observing and analyzing skill and performance for both students and teachers.

QUANTITATIVE TOOLS OF ANALYSIS

The tools of analysis described in this section deal with methods and instruments that allow us to extend our observations by recording them for subsequent measurement and quantifiable analysis.

Both kinematic and kinetic factors can be quantified through the use of two broad types of observational tools: photographic and electromechanical. Table 5 incorporates the levels of analysis discussed in Chapter Four and gives an example of the "type of observation/recording" and the "technique of observation/recording" used within each level of analysis. This table is by no means exhaustive, but it does show the more common types and techniques of observation and recording employed in quantitative analysis. The reader should review Chapter Four and Table 5 before proceeding to the next sections.

Photographic techniques

Photographic techniques record and measure a series of positions occupied by a point or points on the body or limbs at successive instants

Table 5. Levels of analysis and types and techniques of quantitative analysis

Level of analysis	Types of observation/ recording	Techniques of observation/ recording
Behavioral (domain of psychomotor learning and performance)	Performance measures: Scores Effectiveness Efficiency of goal-accomplishment Consistency of outcome	Accuracy scores Error scores Time on target scores Movement time Reaction time Central tendency Variability
Movement (domain of biomechanics and kinesiology)	Kinematic: Displacement Velocity Acceleration Segmental analysis Direct subjective observation Kinetic: Force production Center of gravity Kinesic: Direct subjective observation Nonverbal communication	Electrogoniometer Accelerometer/velocity High-speed moving pictures—cinematography Open-shutter photography —stroboscopic, light, and tracing Field observation Choriometrics Labanotation Kinesics
Muscular (domain of anatomy, kinesiology, and physiology)	Anatomic representation Muscular actions Muscle physiology Muscle arrangement and function Skeletal and articular action	Palpation Electromyography (EMG) Dissection anatomy
Motor (domain of neuropsychology and neurophysiology)	Neural activity change: Information processing Localization of function	Electroencephalography (EEG)* Evoked potential (EP)* Contingent negative variation (CNV)* Reaction time (RT)* Premotor/motor time*

*Usually thought of as indirect measures when human subjects are involved.

in time. The specific technique employed, be it high-speed cinematography, open-shutter photography, stroboscopic photography, light-tracing photography, etc., will depend upon the type of questions asked and the information needed to answer the questions.

Photographic techniques have been used extensively as a means of permanently recording skill and performance for later description or measurement. These techniques are an excellent bridge between the qualitative techniques previously described and the quantitative techniques that follow; they allow us to describe and measure our observations. Dependent upon the specific technique, various types of measurements are taken from the film, by projection, by prints, and so on. Regardless of the photographic technique, an important underlying assumption about film recording must be understood. The pattern of movement of a point at successive instants in time is not necessarily precisely determined. The points are successive and are made up of a series of finite displacements occupying finite time intervals. For measurement, we therefore look at displacements of points, arbitrarily defined, as they move from some initial position. The displacement of points can then be measured in terms of a Cartesian coordinate system[1] or some form of angular measurement. Time is usually implicit, and the displacements are often plotted against time. In general, four types of measurement can be obtained from photographic recording: (1) spatial and temporal patterns of the movement, (2) angular movement plotted against time, (3) angular movement plotted against angular movement, and (4) force and center of gravity calculations. *Cinematography* and *open-shutter photography* are the two broad types of photographic instrumentation. The purpose of each is to record successive points of displacement.

The most common technique employed in study of human movement is cinematography. This technique involves the use of a high-speed movie camera (usually 16 millimeter with speeds of at least 64 frames per second and sometimes up to 500 frames per second). Figs. 3-1 and 3-2 are examples of two forms of cinematographic data reproduction. Specific anatomic points are selected for plotting based upon the ease of photographic observation and the question being asked. The movement through space of the selected points are plotted separately but with the same abscissa (*x* coordinate) and ordinate (*y* coordinate) values.

An inherent limitation with cinematography is that we are measuring an essentially three-dimensional event from a two-dimensional recording. Authors such as Plagenhoeff (1971), Noss (1967), and Miller and Nelson (1973) have suggested specific calculations or instrumentation techniques, such as employment of two cameras, that attempt to minimize or eliminate this limitation. The problem is particularly serious when the researcher desires precisely to calculate the forces involved, the pattern of movement in terms of displacement, velocity, or acceleration, or the angular changes.

In our research at Motor Learning Laboratory, Teachers College we have been interested not in precise patterns of movement but rather in the relative changes in the pattern of movement as a function of practice and environmental condition and in relation to behavioral outcome and change (Higgins and Spaeth, 1972; Spaeth, 1973). The basic assumption with regard to measurement is that the third dimension will be reflected in a relative fashion in two-dimensional film recording.

Our basic technique involves filming the performer from the desired position and then plotting, using an x-y coordinate system, specific predetermined points on a segment or at a joint. In this way we establish a relative amount of movement at each point for a specific frame for the total movement. By obtaining a simple mean and standard deviation for all x and y values for each frame we look at the changes in variability of the movement over practice under differing environmental conditions. An extension of this work involves curve fitting to the mean x, y values for blocks of trials over practice. This is a higher order of analysis and is beyond the scope of this presentation. Application of this technique affords us a way of evaluating changes in movement in relation to behavioral outcomes.

This technique also allows us to determine the relative phasic relationships between segments participating in a movement. By determining the points of initiation of movement in successive segments and their spatial and temporal relationship we have another way of viewing development of motor skill, motor control, and coordination.

The angle-angle measurement technique developed by two English investigators, Cavanaugh and Grieve (1973), has not as yet received much attention. It allows the researcher to analyze the changes in patterns of movement. These authors feel that many measurement techniques, while highlighting some aspects and details of the pattern of movement, are often insensitive to the important details that convey information about the more elusive spatial and temporal changes and differences in patterns of movement. The angle-angle method involves graphically plotting the angle of one limb (abscissa) against the angle of another limb (ordinate) for the same point in time (or frame). This method of measurement is more sensitive than the traditional method of plotting the angle (ordinate) against time (abscissa).

This technique is well suited for descriptive and quantitative purposes. The astute observer can readily see differences in successive patterns of movements, and the patterns can be quantified when needed by performing mathematical and statistical procedures for determining mathematical functions for each pattern.

Two additional photographic techniques are relatively common and hence worthy of brief description. Both relate to open-shutter photography. A regular 35 millimeter (or larger) camera is used, and the shutter is left open for the entire sequence of the movement. *Stroboscopic photography* employs a strobe light flashing at a set rate and exposes a single film with multiple pictures throughout the sequence of the movement (see Miller and Nelson, 1973). The photographic environment is usually dimmed. Measurements can then be taken from a single enlarged photograph. Light tracing is similar except that the performance takes place in a darkened room and small, pen-sized lights are attached to appropriate landmarks on the performer's body and limbs (Prior and Cooper, 1969). A single flash usually exposes an instant in time on the film in order to provide a body limb reference on the resulting photograph. When an enlarged photograph is studied, the pen-lights scribe a series of continuous lines across the picture that depict the pattern of movement for a particular skill.

Photographic techniques and particularly cinematography are some of the more popular forms of recording movement. With the continued development of measurement techniques and instrumentation for obtaining reliable, easily obtainable data, photographic techniques can continue to provide the teacher and researcher with one of the more powerful tools available for studying movements.

Electromechanical techniques

Electromechanical techniques and instrumentation comprise a vast and complex area. Of necessity our discussion will be limited to a brief statement about two techniques for recording movement electromechanically: electromyography and electrogoniometry.

Electromyography (EMG) is a relatively common technique used to record the electrical activity in a contracting muscle (see Basmajian, 1962). EMG is the most peripheral representation of central nervous system function and hence can be a powerful tool for analysis dealing with motor control. In addition, it has been extensively used as a means of evaluating muscle function in relation to specific types of movements: sports skills, laboratory tasks, and so on. Several authors have employed EMG as a means of evaluating skill acquisition (Higgins, 1970a; Kamon, 1966; Kamon and Gormley, 1968).

Electromyographic recordings can be obtained by placing needles directly into the desired muscle or by placing an electrode directly over the muscle or muscle group (surface EMG). Surface EMG, most common in nonmedical environments, records the sum of the muscular electrical activity beneath a pair of electrodes. The magnitude and duration of activity varies as a function of the number and firing rate of the motor units involved and their duration in the muscular contraction.

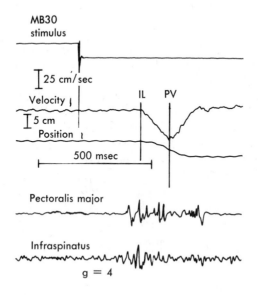

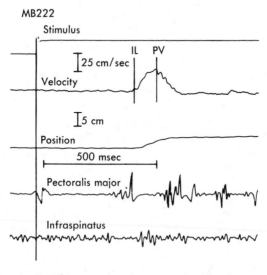

Fig. 9-4. Electromyographic record with step track and velocity and position of movements—tracking task after practice.

The quantitative aspects of EMG are primarily the result of the development of electronic technology and the feasibility of computer application.

The monitoring of EMG signals affords a practical means of determining temporally and spatially the way in which the central nervous system orders its output (Higgins, 1970a). Establishing relationships by observations over time between EMG response and behavioral outcome enables the researcher to evaluate movement behavior in relation to neuromuscular changes occurring during practice or performance (Fig. 9-4). Changes in motor performance appear to be reflected in the patterns of EMG response (Harter et al., 1966).

In recent years the Springfield College group has developed the electrogoniometer (Adrian, 1968; Gollnick and Karpovich, 1964; Sinning and Forsyth, 1970). It is used to measure joint angle or displacement during performance. Essentially, the electrogoniometer is a variable resistor or potentiometer (much like the volume control on a radio) called a "pot," that is connected to two rigid arms. One moves the resistor and the other is connected to the case holding the resistor. The arms are then attached to successive limb segments of the performer with the "pot" over the joint in such fashion that the movement of either segment is reflected in a turning of the "pot." A low voltage signal passes through the "pot," and as the resistance changes due to joint displacement, the voltage will vary accordingly. This voltage signal is then recorded on a suitable polygraph or oscilloscope, and measurement can be made from the graphically reproduced signals.

Basically then, the electrogoniometer records angular displacement between two successive limb segments. This displacement information can be used to evaluate a specific skill, or more importantly, it can be used to evaluate progressive changes in performance over time. Since a temporal component is built into the recording system, simple calculations will also provide velocity information.

In summary, only those tools of analysis have been discussed that can provide data about the movement itself. The many tools that have been developed to measure the forces that produce the movement have not been discussed.

NOTES

1. The Cartesian coordinate system, developed by Rene Descartes in the early 1600s, is a means of graphically representing a point in two- or three-dimensional space by identifying the point with reference to its point of intersection with two or three perpendicular planes, denoted x, y, and z.

TEN

Epilogue: study of human movement and facilitation of skill

This book has attempted to provide an integrative basis for understanding the organization and structure of human movement. This has included an analytic approach for determining the functional characteristics of movements and the constraints and underlying processes responsible for the organization of movements. The primary concern has been to expose the reader to an approach that encompasses the basic theoretical formulation related to concepts and principles for spatial and temporal regulation of goal-directed movements.

The basic theoretical formulations and assumptions have been developed through the preceding nine chapters. It now behooves us to summarize the state of the art with some attention to practical application. Our only means of expressing ideas is by acting upon or in concert with the environment through movements. Therefore, we must understand that analysis of movement is a viable approach for making inferences about the organization of movement. The teacher may find the following points useful in structuring instruction, analyzing learning and acquisition, evaluating performance, and providing appropriate feedback.

The organization of movement is reflected in the spatial and temporal components of the pattern of movement. Patterns of movement can be differentiated in relation to the specific environmental constraints involved; at the same time, they become more consistent with practice. Little information is yet available that allows us to say much about the interaction or order of importance of the morphologic and biomechanical constraints in development of motoric behavior.

As students practice a particular skill, the teacher should observe a continuously less constrained and restricted pattern of movement. Practice might be structured so that students understand the uniqueness of their own movements and the need to develop consistent patterns of movement in relation to the environmental condition. The teacher should also direct attention to the important, identifiable, spatial and temporal components of the movement for each skill. The learner's attention might be focused upon either the spatial or the temporal parameters of the movement. For example, temporal control of the movement (speed, timing, force) may be more important than spatial control of the movement (form) in learning to throw the baseball from the outfield. As temporal control is achieved, attention to spatial control may be the more important element to focus attention upon. Finally, the teacher will want practice conditions to simulate the eventual performance environment as closely as possible so that patterns of movement develop naturally in relation to the environmental situation and stimuli.

The regulatory effect of the environment is of vital importance for successful performance and is reflected in the performers pattern of movement. Spatial components imposed by the environment appear to be reflected in the spatial components of the movement. The temporal components of the environment likewise appear to be reflected in the temporal dimensions of the movement. Thus, there is an assumed relationship between spatial and temporal components of the movement. The spatial and temporal dimensions of the performance environment are a major determinant of the dynamic features of the pattern of movement. Biomechanical and morphologic constraints should not be minimized as important factors in spatial and temporal organization of patterns of movement.

This concept relates to the predictability of the environment. Teachers will want to give attention to the relative importance of spatial versus temporal versus spatial-temporal demands imposed by the environment. For example, in an activity such as golf the spatial characteristics of the environment—ball position—are the regulatory stimuli; hence, attention to the development of a consistent pattern of movement for swinging the club in relation to a predictable ball position (the ball does not move in time and space) is important. In an activity such as tennis, where the spatial and temporal elements of the environment are less predictable, the teacher will focus upon development of a variety of patterns of movement in relation to a variety of spatial-temporal combinations. Practice leading to diversity of pattern of movement may initially be more important than the consistency of pattern of movement.

Each performer, for each skill, will exhibit a different pattern of movement dependent upon morphology and the imposed environmental and biomechanical constraints. Performers must learn to deal with their unique morphologic constraints. The performer's morphology is also considered in relation to the biomechanical constraints inherent in the task or skill. For example, when learning a serve in tennis a short performer develops a pattern of movement that matches not only his morphology (height and short limb segments) but also the imposed biomechanical constraints (angle of ball trajectory, height of net). Morphologically, the performer's limbs are shorter than those of the tall performer, and this will affect the potential power through the application of muscular force on the lever system. The height from which the ball can be contacted will also differ between the short and tall performer; the angle of service trajectory and effective target area for successful performance is thus a limiting factor to overcome in the short performer's service.

Level of skill for each performer and type of skill will influence the resultant pattern of movement. Level and type of skill will have an important effect upon the performer's pattern of movement. The teacher should consider both when structuring the learning environment for instruction or practice. For example, practice in the golf swing should be structured with attention to form during early stages of learning, with power or force becoming more important as learning progresses. In badminton, form is not as important in the early stages of learning as production of force and coincidence with the environmental stimuli (contact with the shuttlecock). Similar considerations need to be given to each classified skill before efficient and meaningful instruction and practice can take place.

Patterns of movement appear to be organized by first establishing body stability and transport patterns; limb manipulatory patterns are then superimposed upon this foundation. As the emerging pattern of movement develops, the effectiveness of goal accomplishment seems to be a function of the formation of a stable and consistent base of support with respect to body stability and transport. Effectiveness and decreased variability of limb manipulation appears to lag behind concomitent patterns of movement for the body. For example, effective goal accomplishment in a young child learning to hit a baseball seems to develop only after the stance and body movement become more stable and consistent. The development of differentiated and consistent patterns of movements for limb manipulation seems to coincide with this body stability function. It would appear that teachers might therefore emphasize body stability and transport functions early in practice. As this function stabilizes, the emphasis can shift to the limb manipulation functions. This is not to suggest, however, that limb manipulation should be ignored early in practice.

Systematic analysis of movement, especially direct subjective analysis, should lead to the facilitation of development of skill. This seems intuitively reasonable for the following reasons: (1) the student learns a systematic form of self-movement analysis; (2) the teacher understands and identifies the specific and important components of the movement and thus has a means of generalizing for instruction; (3) the teacher can focus upon components of skill most relevant to the individual performer, to the performer's level of skill, and to the specific skill; (4) evaluation of movement and feedback appropriate to the skill and learner are more easily identified; and (5) another dimension of skill learning can be assessed.

Analysis of the interaction between the moving organism and defined constraints leads toward understanding of movement. Through analysis we can understand: (1) environmental parameters influencing the moving organism; (2) physical capacities of the performer (morphology) in relation to specific skills and level of skill; (3) ability of the performer to obtain environmental information, process that information, and produce appropriate and effective motoric responses (sensory-motor integration); (4) how learning and acquisition progresses by identifying progressive changes in patterns of movement, behavioral outcome, and their interrelationships; (5) coordinated movement, organization of movement, and motor control processes; and (6) individual differences in performance and development of motor skill.

An example from basketball will illustrate this concept. In the game situation the environment is spatially and temporally unpredictable (S/T). The coach wants a "playmaker" and may select the performer who plays a guard (or outside) position. A guard is usually shorter than other performers (morphology) and is successful because his style of play is adapted to his morphologic constraints (he is quick, can dribble well, etc.). An effective playmaker can process information from the total environmental situation and can choose and execute an appropriate play, quickly modify game plans, or completely change plans according to his immediate predictions of the playing situation; he exhibits good sensory-motor integration. As the game or practice progresses, he easily learns from his experiences and integrates this information into his overall performance. The playmaker is coordinated, his movements are deceptive, he feints well and smoothly and efficiently moves up and down the court. Finally, he recognizes individual differences, as does the coach or teacher, not only on his own team but also among his opponents.

A central objective throughout our exploration of human movement has been to focus upon issues and theories related to the organization of movement. We should continue our relentless pursuit for understanding the ways in which variation and consistencies in performance are reflected in patterns of movement, behavior, and neuromuscular insights.

Hopefully the preceding chapters have moved our thinking about human movement in directions that will fulfill the practical needs of the teacher as well as those interested in continued research in this important and fruitful area of study. I have attempted to break a pervasive set existing in both biomechanics and psychomotor skill learning—namely to move beyond thinking about motor skill in terms of behavioral outcomes or simple mechanical analysis of specific skills. This mission will have been accomplished if the reader can now view the study of human movement as a process of complex interacting constraints, level of skill, type of movement, and appropriate levels of analysis; it is *not* simply the outcome of a movement that is important but also the manner in which that outcome was produced. Our view of the study of human movement must therefore be multidimensional. This direction will aid in the establishment of meaningful relationships between performance outcomes and the contributory factors upon which organization of movement is dependent.

BIBLIOGRAPHY

Adrian, M. J. An introduction to electrogoniometry. *Kinesiology Review*, Washington, D.C.: American Association of Health, Physical Education and Recreation, 1968.

Arend, S., and Higgins, J. R. A strategy for the classification, subjective analysis and observation of human movement. *Journal of Human Movement Studies*, 1976, *2*, 36–52.

Barker, D. The innervation of the muscle spindle. *Quarterly Journal of Microscopic Science*, 1948, *89*, 143–186.

Bartlett, F. C. The measurement of human skill. *British Journal of Medicine*, 1947a, *1*, 835–838.

Bartlett, F. C. The measurement of human skill. *British Journal of Medicine*, 1947b, *1*, 877–880.

Basmajian, J. V. *Muscles alive* (2nd ed.). Baltimore: Williams & Wilkins Co., 1962.

Basmajian, J. V. Control of individual motor units. *American Journal of Physical Medicine*, 1967, *46*, 480–486.

Basmajian, J. V. Electromyographic analyses of basic movement patterns. In J. Wilmore (Ed.), *Exercise and sport sciences reviews*. New York: Academic Press, 1973.

Bernstein, N. *The coordination and regulation of movement*. Oxford: Pergamon Press, Ltd., 1967.

Birdwhistle, R. L. *Kinesics and context: essays on body communication*. Philadelphia: University of Philadelphia Press, 1970.

Bizzi, E. The coordination of eye-head movements. *Scientific American*, 1974, *231*, 100–106.

Broer, M. R. *Efficiency of human movement*. Philadelphia: W. B. Saunders Co., 1968.

Bruner, J. S. The growth and structure of skill. In K. Connoly (Ed.), *Mechanisms of motor skill development*. New York: Academic Press, 1971.

Cavanaugh, P. R., and Grieve, D. W. The graphical display of angular movement of the body. *British Journal of Sports Medicine*, 1973, *7*, 129–133.

Cooper, J. M. (Ed.). *Selected topics on biomechanics*. Proceedings of the C. I. C. Symposium on biomechanics, Indiana University, 1970. Chicago: Athletic Institute, 1971.

Cooper, J., and Glassow, R. B. *Kinesiology* (4th ed.) St. Louis: The C. V. Mosby Co., 1976.

Counsilman, J. E. *The science of swimming*. Englewood Cliffs, N.J.: Prentice-Hall, Inc., 1968.

Davidovits, P. *Physics in biology and medicine*. Englewood Cliffs, N.J.: Prentice-Hall, Inc., 1975.

Easton, T. A. On the normal use of reflexes. *American Scientist*, 1972, *60*, 591–599.

144

Eccles, J. C. *The understanding of the brain.* New York: McGraw-Hill Book Company, 1973.

Evarts, E. V., and Thach, W. T. Strategies and tactics in research on central control of movement. *Neurosciences Research Progress Bulletin,* 1971, 9, 113–139.

Feather, N. *Matter and motion: physical sciences—physics.* Baltimore: Penguin Books, 1970.

Fitts, P. M. Perceptual-motor skill learning. In A. W. Melton (Ed.), *Categories of human learning.* New York: Academic Press, 1964.

Gagne, R. M., and Fleishman, E. A. *Psychology and human performance.* New York: Holt, Rinehart and Winston, 1959.

Gelfand, J. M. [*Models of the structural-functional organization of certain biological systems*] (V. S. Gurfinkel, S. V. Fromin, and M. L. Tsetlin, Eds.) (C. R. Reed, Trans.). Cambridge, Mass.: The M.I.T. Press, 1971.

Gentile, A. M. A working model of skill acquisition with application to teaching. *Quest,* 1972, 17, 3–23.

Gentile, A. M., Higgins, J. R., Miller, E. A., and Rosen, B. M. Structure of motor tasks. *Movement, Actes du 7ᵉ symposium en apprentissage psycho-moteur et psychologie du sport,* October 1975, 11–28.

Gentile, A. M., and Nacson, J. Organizational processes in motor control. In J. Keogh (Ed.), *Exercise and sport sciences reviews.* Santa Barbara, Calif.: Journal Publishing Affiliates, 1976.

Gollnick, P. D., and Karpovich, P. V. Electrogoniometric study of locomotion and some athletic movements. *Research Quarterly,* 1964, 35, 357–369.

Granit, R. *Receptors and sensory perception.* New Haven: Yale University Press, 1955.

Granit, R. *The basis of motor control.* New York: Academic Press, 1970.

Gregory, R. L. *Eye and brain: the psychology of seeing.* New York: McGraw-Hill Book Company, 1966.

Harter, M., Russell, S., and White, C. T. Periodicity within reaction times and electromyograms. *Quarterly Journal of Experimental Psychology,* 1966, 20, 157–167.

Hartson, L. D. Contrasting approaches to the analysis of skilled movement. *Journal of General Psychology,* 1939, 20, 263–293.

Hay, J. G. *The biomechanics of sports techniques.* Englewood Cliffs, N.J.: Prentice-Hall, Inc., 1973.

Hefferline, R. F., Bruno, L. J. J., and Davidowitz, J. E. Feedback control of covert behavior. In K. J. Connoly (Ed.), *Mechanisms of motor skill development.* New York: Academic Press, 1971.

Henneman, E. Organization of the motor systems: a preview. In V. B. Mountcastle (Ed.), *Medical Physiology* (13th ed.) (Vol II). St. Louis: The C. V. Mosby Co., 1974.

Henneman, E. Peripheral mechanisms involved in the control of muscle. In V. B. Mountcastle (Ed.), *Medical physiology* (13th ed.) (Vol II). St. Louis: The C. V. Mosby Co. 1974.

Higgins, J. R. Performance phenomena involved in arresting errors in movement. Doctoral dissertation, Stanford University, 1970a.

Higgins, J. R. *Biomechanics and motor learning.* Paper presented at the First Motor Learning Symposium, Teachers College, Columbia University, New York City, February 1970b.

Higgins, J. R. Movements to match environmental demands. *Research Quarterly,* 1972, 43, 312–336.

Higgins, J. R., and Spaeth, R. K. Relationship between consistency of movement and environmental condition. *Quest,* 1972, 17, 61–69.

Hoffman, S. J. The effects of practice on variability in movement: a cinematographic analysis. Doctoral dissertation, Teachers College, Columbia University, 1971.

Hopper, B. J. *The mechanics of human movement*. New York: American Elsevier Publishing Company, Inc., 1973.

Houk, J., and Henneman, E. Feedback control of movement and posture. In V. B. Mountcastle (Ed.), *Medical physiology* (13th ed.) (Vol. II). St. Louis: The C. V. Mosby Co., 1974.

Howard, I. P., and Templeton, W. B. *Human spatial orientation*. New York: John Wiley & Sons, 1966.

Hubbard, A. W. Homokinetics: muscular function in human movement. In W. R. Johnson (Ed.), *Science and medicine of exercise and sports*. New York: Harper & Brothers, Publishers, 1960.

International seminar on biomechanics II. (J. Vredenbregt and J. Wartenweiler, Eds.). Baltimore: University Park Press, 1971.

International seminar on biomechanics III. (S. Ceroquiglini, A. Venerando, and J. Wartenweiler, Eds.). Baltimore: University Park Press, 1973.

International seminar on biomechanics IV. (R. C. Nelson and C. A. Morehouse, Eds.). Baltimore: University Park Press, 1974.

Ito, M. Neurophysiological aspects of the cerebellar motor control system. *International Journal of Neurology*, 1970, 7, 162–173.

Kamon, E. Electromyography analysis of the scissors exercise performed on the pommel horse. *The Journal of Sports Medicine and Physical Fitness*, 1966, 6, 223–234.

Kamon, E., and Gormley, J. Muscular activity pattern for skilled performance and during learning of a horizontal bar exercise. *Ergonomics*, 1968, 11, 345–357.

Kay, H. The development of motor skills from birth to adolescence. In E. A. Bilodeau (Ed.), *Principles of skill acquisition*. New York: Academic Press, 1969.

Kay, H. Analyzing motor skill performance. In K. Connoly (Ed.), *Mechanisms of motor skill development*. New York: Academic Press, 1971.

Knapp, B. *Skill in sport, the attainment of proficiency*. London: Routledge and Kegan Paul, 1963.

Konorski, J. *Integrative activity of the brain*. Chicago: University of Chicago Press, 1967.

Logan, G. A., and McKinney, W. C. *Kinesiology*. Dubuque, Iowa: Wm. C. Brown, 1970.

Lomax, A., Bartenieff, I., and Pauley, F. Choreometrics: a method and the study of cross cultural patterns in film. *Research Film*, 1969, 6, 505-517.

Lorenz, K. Z. Innate bases of learning. In K. H. Pribram (Ed.), *On the biology of learning*. New York: Harcourt, Brace, and World, 1969.

Luria, A. R. The complex mechanisms of physiological processes. Impact of science on society: UNESCO. Vol. XVIII, No. 3, July-September 1968, pp. 141-156.

MacConaill, M. A., and Basmajian, J. V. *Muscles and movements: a basis for human kinesiology*. Baltimore: Williams and Wilkins, Co., 1969.

Miller, D. L., and Nelson, R. C. *Biomechanics of sport: a research approach*. Philadelphia: Lea & Febiger, 1973.

Miller, G. A., Galanter, E., and Pribram, K. *Plans and the structure of behavior*. New York: Holt, Rinehart, and Winston, 1960.

Mountcastle, V. B. (Ed.). *Medical physiology* (13th ed.). St. Louis: The C. V. Mosby Co., 1974.

Nixon, J. E., and Locke, L. F. Research on teaching physical education. In R. M. W. Travers (Ed.), *Handbook of research on teaching*. Chicago: Rand McNally, 1973.

Northrup, J. W., Logan, G. A., and McKinney, W. C. *Introduction to biomechanic analysis of sport*. Dubuque, Iowa: Wm. C. Brown Company, 1974.

Noss, J. Control of photographic perspective. *Journal of Health, Physical Education and Recreation*, 1967, 38, 81–84.

Patton, H. D. Reflex regulation of movement and posture. In T. C. Ruch, H. D. Patton, J.

Bibliography 147

W. Woodbury, and A. L. Towe, *Neurophysiology.* Philadelphia: W. B. Saunders Company, 1966.

Plagenhoeff, S. *Patterns of human motion.* Englewood Cliffs, N.J.: Prentice-Hall, Inc., 1971.

Poulton, E. C. On prediction in skilled movements. *Psychological Bulletin,* 1957, *54,* 467–478.

Pribram, K. *Language of the brain.* Englewood Cliffs, N.J.: Prentice-Hall, Inc., 1972.

Prior, T., and Cooper, J. M. Light tracing used as a tool in analysis of human movement. *Research Quarterly,* 1969, *39,* 815–817.

Quest. Learning models and the acquisition of motor skills. 1972, *17.*

Rasch, P. J., and Burke, R. K. *Kinesiology and applied anatomy.* Philadelphia: Lea & Febiger, 1974.

Research Quarterly. Skill learning and performance. 1972, *43.*

Roebuck, J. A. Kinesiology in engineering. *Kinesiology Review,* Washington, D.C.: American Association of Health, Physical Education and Recreation, 1968.

Ruch, T. C., Patton, H. D., Woodbury, J. W., and Towe, A. L. *Neurophysiology.* Philadelphia, W. B. Saunders Co., 1966.

Schleihauf, R. A biomechanical analysis of freestyle. *Swimming Techniques,* Fall 1974, *2,* 89–96.

Schleihauf, R. Hydrodynamic analysis of breaststroke pulling proficiency. *Swimming Technique,* Winter 1976, *12,* 100–105.

Sherrington, C. *The integrative action of the nervous system.* New Haven: Yale University Press, 1961.

Sinning, W. E., and Forsyth, H. L. Lower limb actions while running at different velocities. *Medicine and Science in Sports,* 1970, *2,* 28–34.

Sommerhoff, G. *Logic of the living brain.* New York: John Wiley & Sons, 1974.

Spaeth, R. K. Maximizing goal attainment. *Research Quarterly,* 1972, *43,* 337–361.

Spaeth, R. K. Skill acquisition under variable temporal constraints: cinematographic analysis of movement organization. Doctoral dissertation, Teachers College, Columbia University, 1973.

Sperry, R. W. Neurology and the mind-brain problem. *American Scientist,* 1952, *40,* 291–312.

Stark, L. *Neurological control systems: studies in bioengineering.* New York: Plenum Press, 1968.

Steindler, A. *Kinesiology of the human body.* Springfield, Ill.: Charles C Thomas, Publisher, 1955.

Thompson, R. F. *Foundations of physiological psychology.* New York: Harper & Row, Publishers, 1967.

Toyoshima, S., Hoshikawa, T., Miyashita, M., and Oguri, T. Contribution of the body parts to throwing performance. In R. C. Nelson and C. A. Morehouse (Eds.), *International seminar on biomechanics IV.* Baltimore: University Park Press, 1974.

Tricker, R. A. R., and Tricker, B. S. K. *The science of movement.* New York: American Elsevier Publishing Co., 1967.

Vaughn, H. G., Jr., and Ritter, W. Physiologic approaches to the analysis of attention and performance. In S. Kornblum (Ed.), *Attention and Performance IV.* New York: Academic Press, 1973.

Walter, W. G. The electrical activity of the brain. *Scientific American,* 1954, *190*(6), 54–63.

Welford, A. T. *Fundamentals of skill.* London: Methuen & Co., 1968.

Wells, K. F. *Kinesiology.* Philadelphia: W. B. Saunders Co., 1971.

Wells, K. F., and Luttgens, K. *Kinesiology.* Philadelphia: W. B. Saunders Co., 1976.

INDEX

Brain stem, 55
Buoyancy, effect of, on movement through
    water, 98-99

C

Cancellous tissue in bone, 104-105
Cardiac muscle, 61
Cartilage, articular, 107
Cell body of neuron, 57-58
Central nervous system, 55-56
    in control of movement, 69-73
    in coordination of movement, 32-34
Cerebellar hemispheres, 55
Cerebellum, function of, in movement, 71-
    72
Cerebral cortex, 55
    functions of, in movement, 72
Cerebral hemispheres, 55
Character, classification of movements ac-
    cording to, 20
Cinematography in quantitative analysis of
    movement, 134-135
Closed skills, 77
Compact bone, 104-105
Constraints
    on movement, 43-48
    biomechanical, 45-46; *see also* Biome-
        chanical constraints
    environmental, 45; *see also* Environ-
        mental constraints
    morphologic, 46; *see also* Morphologic
        constraints
    and moving organism, interaction be-
        tween, analysis of, in understand-
        ing movement, 142-143
Constructs
    biomechanical; *see* Biomechanical con-
        struct
    in learning skill, 85
Contraction(s)
    isometric, definition of, 21
    isotonic, definition of, 21
    of muscle fibers, events leading to, 60
    of muscle in movement, 112
    philometric, definition of, 21
Contralateral muscle group, function of, 112
Coordination of human movement, 29-40

D

Dendrites of neuron, 57-58
Depolarization in contraction of muscle fi-
    ber, 60
Descriptive analysis of skill and perfor-
    mance, 125-126
Diarthrodial articulations, 105-107
Diencephalon, 55
Direct adaptive movements, 23

Direct subjective analysis of movement,
    126-132
    in facilitation of skill development, 141-
        142
Direction, intended, application of maxi-
    mum force and speed in, 92-93
Drag force in movement through water, 100
Dynamics
    definition of, 4
    of movement, 21

E

Efferent component of nervous system, 57
Efferent neurons, functions of, 58
Electrogoniometer in quantitative analysis
    of movement, 138
Electromechanical techniques in quantita-
    tive analysis of movement, 136-138
Electromyography in quantitative analysis
    of movement, 136-138
Environment
    moment-to-moment condition of, as
        source of variation in movement,
        35
    and movements, 81-83
    nature of, relation of type of movement
        to, system for, 22-28
    predictability of, 79-81
    regulatory effect of, on performance, 140
Environmental constraints, 45
    behavioral and movement levels of anal-
        ysis in relation to, 51-52
    effects of, on movement, 46-48
    in organization of movement, 75-83
    spatial and temporal elements as, 78-79
Equatorial region of muscle spindle, 63-65
Equipment
    as environmental constraint, 45, 78
    as morphologic compensating factor, 116
Ergonomic cycle in summation of internal
    forces, 88-90
Excitation-conduction coupling, 60
Exteroreceptors, functions of, 61
Extrafusal muscle fibers
    function of, 63
    length of, control of, 65

F

Fasciae, 110
Feedback, sensory, for adjustments in mus-
    cular actions, 62
Fibers, muscle; *see* Muscle fibers
Flight pattern of body in space, 97-98
Follow-through
    in segmental analysis of movement, 122,
        123
    as stage of ergonomic cycle, 88

R

Reaction, law of, 87
Rebound, angle of, factors affecting, 98
Receptors, 61-68
Redundancy in movement organization, 80
Reflexes and purposeful human movement, 68-69
Return stage of ergonomic cycle, 88
Rib cage in segmental analysis of movement, 122, 123
Rules as environmental constraint, 45, 78

S

Saccule, function of, 68
Sagittal plane of motion, 13, 14, 15, 16, 17
Segmental analysis of movement, 121-122, 123
Semicircular canals, function of, 68
Sensory component of nervous system, 57
Sensory feedback for adjustments in muscular actions, 62
Sensory neurons, functions of, 58
Sensory pathways in cerebral cortex, 72-73
Sex
    as morphologic constraints, 114
    organismic variable of, behavioral and muscular levels of analysis in relation to, 53
Shoulder area in segmental analysis of movement, 122, 123
Skeletal muscle, 61
    motor unit and, 59-61
Skeletal system, structure, design and composition of, 104-109
Skill(s)
    analysis of, 120
        multidimensional, 50-53
    classification of, composite model for, 22-28
    closed, 24-26, 77
    in context of biomechanics, 9-11
    definition of, 9-10
    descriptive analysis of, 125-126
    development of, facilitation of, analysis of movement in, 141-142
    facilitation of, study of human movement and, 139-143
    level and type of, effect of, on pattern of movement, 141
    open, 24-25, 26
Smooth muscle, 61
Soma of neuron, 57-58
Somatic afferent neurons, function of, 58
Somatic efferent neurons, functions of, 58
Somesthetic/proprioceptive sensory information resulting from movement-produced stimulation, 62-63

Somesthetic/proprioceptive system, 67
Space
    body in, flight pattern of, 97-98
    definition of, 94
    object projected in, flight patterns of, 95-97
Spatial characteristics of movement, 21
Spatial components of pattern of movement as reflection of movement organization, 139-140
Spatial configuration of environment, 45
Spatial elements
    of environment, 76-78
    as regulatory factors, 78-79
Special afferent neurons, function of, 58
Speed
    maximum, application of, in intended direction, 92-93
    transfer of, to succeeding segments, 90-92
Spinal cord, 55-56
Stabilizing muscles, function of, 112
Statics, definition of, 4
Stimulation, movement-produced, 62
Stroboscopic photography in quantitative analysis of movement, 136
Structural analysis of human movement, 7-8
Structural elements of movement, 42-43
Structural unity in coordination of movement, 33
Structural-functional relationship and morphologic constraints, 103-104
Summation of internal forces
    base of support and, 93-94
    biochemical construct of, 87-94
    biomechanical goal of movement and, 89
    body center of gravity and, 93-94
    ergonomic cycle in, 88-90
Synaptic cleft, 58
Synarthrodial articulations, 117

T

Taxonomy of movement, 41
Telodendria, function of, 58
Teloreceptors, functions of, 61
Temporal characteristics of movement, 21
Temporal components of pattern of movement as reflection of movement organization, 139-140
Temporal configuration of environment, 45
Temporal control dimension in classification of movement, 25
Temporal elements
    of environment, 76-78
    as regulatory factors, 78-79
Temporal lobe of cerebral cortex, function of, 72
Tendons, 110

Tension, muscular, Golgi tendon organs in control of, 66-67
Thorax, 104
Time lags as morphologic constraints, 113-114
Transmission, neuromuscular, 60
Transverse plane of motion, 14, 17

U

Unity, structural, in coordination of movement, 33
Utricle, function of, 68

V

Velocity, definition of, 86

Vertebral column, 104
Visceral afferent neurons, function of, 58
Visceral efferent neurons, functions of, 58
Vision, 67-68
Visual sensory information resulting from movement-produced stimulation, 62-63
Visual sensory system, 67-68

W

Water, resistance of, in movement through water, 99